WOOD FOR BIOENERGY

FOREST HISTORY SOCIETY ISSUES SERIES

The Forest History Society was founded in 1946. Since that time, the Society, through its research, reference, and publications programs, has advanced forest and conservation history scholarship. At the same time, it has translated that scholarship into formats useful for people with policy and management responsibilities. For seven decades the Society has worked to demonstrate history's significant utility.

The Forest History Society's Issues Series is one of the Society's most explicit contributions to history's utility. The Society selects issues of importance today that also have significant historical dimensions. Then we invite authors of demonstrated knowledge to examine an issue and synthesize its substantial literature, while keeping the general reader in mind.

The final and most important step is making these authoritative overviews available. Toward that end, an initial distribution is made to people with education, management, policy, or legislative responsibilities who will benefit from a deepened understanding of how a particular issue began and evolved. The books are commonly used in education programs throughout North America and beyond.

The Issues Series—like its Forest History Society sponsor—is nonadvocatory and aims to present a balanced rendition of often contentious issues.

Other Issues Series titles available from the Forest History Society:
American Forests: A History of Resiliency and Recovery
America's Fires: A Historical Context for Policy and Practice
America's Forested Wetlands: From Wasteland to Valued Resource
Canada's Forests: A History
Forest Pharmacy: Medicinal Plants in American Forests
Forest Sustainability: The History, the Challenge, the Promise
Genetically Modified Forests: From Stone Age to Modern Biotechnology
Newsprint: Canadian Supply and American Demand

Electronic resources of the Forest History Society:
www.foresthistory.org
www.peelingbackthebark.org (blog)
www.youtube.com/foresthistory
www.flickr.com/foresthistory
www.twitter.com/foresthistory
www.facebook.com/foresthistory

WOOD FOR

Bioenergy

Forests as a Resource for Biomass and Biofuels

BROOKS C. MENDELL
and AMANDA H. LANG

THE
FOREST
HISTORY
SOCIETY

ISSUES
SERIES

Forest History Society
Durham, North Carolina

The Forest History Society is a nonprofit educational and research institution dedicated to the advancement of historical understanding of human interaction with the forest environment. It was established in 1946. Interpretations and conclusions in FHS publications are those of the authors; the institution takes responsibility for the selection of topics, competency of the authors, and their freedom of inquiry.

This book was published with support from the Plum Creek Foundation, U.S. Forest Service Research, Forest Investment Associates, National Alliance of Forest Owners, Potlatch Corporation, Price Biostock, The Westervelt Company, and the Lynn W. Day Endowment for Forest History Publications.

Printed in the United States of America

Forest History Society
701 William Vickers Avenue
Durham, North Carolina 27701
(919) 682-9319
www.foresthistory.org

©2012 by the Forest History Society

Design by Zubigraphics, Inc.

Library of Congress Cataloging-in-Publication Data

Mendell, Brooks C. (Brooks Collat), 1970- author.
 Wood for bioenergy : forests as a resource for biomass and biofuels / Brooks C. Mendell and Amanda H. Lang.
    pages cm
 ISBN 978-0-89030-076-3 (pbk. : alk. paper)
 1. Fuelwood--United States--History. I. Lang, Amanda H., author. II. Title.
 TP324.M46 2012
 333.95'397--dc23
                        2012030477

CONTENTS

LIST OF FIGURES

These are interesting times for wood bioenergy. Traditional fossil fuels are under attack in the United States for at least two reasons. First is the security issue, as the United States has been increasing its energy imports, particularly of oil, from suppliers of questionable reliability. In addition to Middle East sources, even in the Western Hemisphere some sources raise security issues. In Venezuela the security issues are due to politics, and in Mexico, a reliable supplier for many years, due to the long-term decline in petroleum production. The second issue with fossil fuels is carbon dioxide emissions, which have been linked to global warming. Although biomass releases carbon emissions upon burning, its growth and regeneration collect those released gases. A contentious issue is how policy should treat the recycled gases.

In response to those challenges, much of the world, including the United States, has tried to undertake policies to reduce dependence on fossil fuels. An apparently attractive candidate is renewable energy, three of the most important being wind, solar, and biomass energy. Within the biomass energy group, wood has the potential to play a major role.

Wood bioenergy can come in two basic forms: as direct combustion and as a feedstock to produce liquid fuels, such as ethanol, which can be used for transport. As direct combustion, wood can substitute for fossil fuels in heating applications and electrical production facilities.

Confounding the issue, however, most bioenergy feedstocks have alternative uses. In the United States about 30 percent of the corn crop is used for ethanol production. Corn prices are said to have doubled because of the substantial fuel demand, creating a tension between use for food and use for fuel. Even when not in direct competition for the product, feed-stocks may be in competition for the resources for their production. Most biomass energy feedstock is land intensive. Grains, palm oil, and woody biomass all require substantial land areas, which typically have alternative uses in agriculture.

Today, most biomass liquid fuels in the United States are derived from grains, such as corn. However, cellulosic biomass from grass, agricultural waste, and woody biomass can also produce liquid fuels. Currently, the costs of cellulosic biofuels are high, but technical breakthroughs promise lower future costs.

Given the host of contemporary issues revolving around wood bioen-ergy, Brooks Mendell and Amanda Lang have provided a hugely informative book that could not be more timely. It provides a history of wood energy in the United States and then goes on to cover the various wood energy products: pellets, wood for electrical power, and wood as a feedstock for cellulosic liquid fuels, including ethanol. The discussion includes an under-standable description of cellulosic ethanol technology as well as other processes that can produce liquid biofuels.

Throughout the book various graphs provide useful data on trends and forecasts of various aspects of wood feedstock, bioenergy production, trade, and use. Projections are provided of future bioenergy needs into the mid-dle of the 21st century. Additionally, other useful information is provided throughout the book, such as an inventory of commercial biofuel projects.

The book then focuses on the forest to discuss the various types of wood biomass feedstocks and provide estimates of the wood supply availability. Wood bioenergy markets are discussed as well as public policies. Throughout, the focus remains on the potential of wood as a renewable energy. The dis-cussion of issues around wood bioenergy emissions is very current. Included, for example, is a discussion of the contemporary and controversial issue of the carbon neutrality of the various wood-based forest bioenergies.

This little book provides quick but comprehensive coverage of wood bioenergy issues. It certainly could be titled "Everything you always wanted to know about wood energy" without being overly presumptuous. A quick read could readily inform one about the field and its critical issues. Who might benefit from reading this book? Anyone interested in keeping abreast with forest or energy issues: community leaders who are faced with proposals for plant facilities in their jurisdictions, teachers who are seeking basic information to bring into the classroom, foresters and other natural resource managers who need background for discussing the issue with the public, investors and facility principals who need to make sure their proposals are well founded, and policymakers who will likely determine whether biomass energy can be sustained over time.

Roger Sedjo
Senior Fellow and Director, Forest Economics and Policy
Resources for the Future, Washington, D.C.

Wood has been used as fuel for energy in North America for centuries—first for heating and cooking, then as a fuel for locomotives, steamboats, and stationary engines and in the manufacture of iron and steel. As demand for energy during the Industrial Revolution increased, concern for long-term supplies of wood rose along with consumption rates. Its use as an energy source waned during the mid-twentieth century, only to begin rising in the 1980s and 1990s from increased use for residential and manufacturing purposes. Today, new potential uses of wood biomass and biofuels have put wood in the spotlight once again as a renewable resource. However, the future viability of wood energy relies on sustainable and cost effective supply of woody raw material.

The history of forests as a resource for bioenergy provides foundational insights for future discussion and decision making.

- By the 1800s, factories relied on wood charcoal to generate the heat needed for manufacturing. The use of wood for charcoal complemented economic growth at a time when landowners cleared forestland for agriculture to support the expanding U.S. population. Because of demand for energy during the Industrial Revolution, wood became relatively expensive because it came from ever more remote locations.
- In the early 1900s, wood was increasingly used for building products, such as lumber, and industry shifted to then-plentiful—and thus inexpensive—coal and petroleum fuels for energy. Such transitions are common in energy markets: consumers choose energy sources based on

availability and cost, shifting to the most abundant and cost-effective sources at the time.

- Interest in woody biomass for energy rebounded in response to the oil embargo in 1973. However, when oil prices declined in the mid-1980s, investors' interest in bioenergy receded. Oil price increases following the September 11, 2001, terrorist attacks and U.S. military efforts in the Middle East revived interest in bioenergy, including energy from woody materials.

- Pellets have been manufactured in the United States since the 1970s. Until the early 2000s, most production had been for U.S. consumption. Today, Europe's growing demand for wood pellets drives investments in pellet production and capacity in North America.

- The wood-to-electricity market in the United States continues to develop. Currently, the cost to produce electricity from biomass exceeds the cost to produce electricity from coal or natural gas. The viability of this market therefore depends on public policy, such as mandates for state renewable portfolio standards (RPS) and a proposed federal renewable electricity standard (RES).

- Advanced wood-based biofuels, including ethanol and drop-in alternatives, face multiple technological and logistic challenges. To date, these projects remain unproven at a commercial scale. In addition, financing has been scarce since 2009, leading to high dependence on government-guaranteed debt.

- Environmental groups and forest products firms are concerned about the potential consequences of demand for woody biomass on forest supplies. Researchers have attempted to quantify the volume of U.S. woody biomass available for energy. On a national level, residue from forests, urban trees, and mill processing may be enough to satisfy the need for wood for energy. However, woody raw material supplies for a given community or local wood bioenergy project are subject to local wood market conditions.

- Historically, wood bioenergy was influenced by legislation regulating electric utilities and by efforts to increase U.S. renewable energy generation in the 1970s. More recent policy efforts involve renewable energy targets, emissions permitting, and woody biomass production.

- For the forest products industry, the value of wood raw materials is largely determined by the value of building products, such as lumber, and pulp. Raw material prices are also influenced by the local wood "basket" surrounding their operating facilities. Determining the value of wood is critical because it has implications for forest management, timber harvesting, and wood use. Timberland owners who sell their trees must decide whether to maximize wood volume for pulp mill and sawmill customers or to maximize the wood's energy content for energy customers. From this view, wood bioenergy is another forest product that will merge into the forest products supply chain.

- Two factors could discourage the expanded use of wood for energy. First, bioenergy firms may not have the technology to convert wood to energy cost-effectively, especially for liquid fuels. Second, policy decisions could undermine the market. For example, a policy that subsidizes alternative energy sources, such as nuclear, at higher rates than for wood would make biomass uncompetitive.

- Forest products companies with manufacturing facilities remain uniquely suited for projects involving wood bioenergy and cofiring (burning wood alongside coal). These companies create their own fuel through procurement and manufacturing processes. They have experience and history in managing permitting issues associated with air and water. And they have the ability to manage logistic issues, such as trucking and processing.

- Currently, the established wood raw material procurement system is designed and organized to deliver primarily roundwood (logs) and mill residue to forest products facilities. The collection and delivery of logging residue and, to a certain degree, in-woods chips, are localized and not common in some places.

- Bioenergy facilities depend on logging residue, mill residue, and in-woods chips to satisfy their raw material needs. In turn, these sources are generated from log harvesting and lumber production. As a result, if no one harvests the primary roundwood for logs or produces lumber, the supplies of residual raw materials needed by woody biomass facilities may not be available.

Anyone who has ever roasted a marshmallow while camping or warmed a room from a fireplace knows that heat—and energy— is simply a match, an old newspaper, and a few logs away. The energy fueled by forest resources in the form of wood changed history. The ability to harness forest resources for energy applications allowed people to produce heat and light at will, raising standards of living and ultimately jump-starting the industrial age.

Wood bioenergy—which includes the production of electricity, liquid fuels, and pellets from woody biomass—creates issues, opportunities, and decisions for a range of stakeholders. The renewable nature of woody raw material enhances its status as an attractive, relatively inexpensive fuel source. Yet communities, landowners, power companies, forestry professionals, investors, and policymakers struggle to make decisions with scattered information about the status of wood bioenergy in the United States and throughout North America.

The current interest in using wood for energy is not new; in fact, Americans have used wood for fuel for centuries. Until the second half of the 19th century, wood was virtually the only fuel used in this country (MacCleery 1992). In addition to heating and cooking, wood was used as a transportation fuel for locomotives, steamboats, and stationary engines. The recent enthusiasm for wood depends on the assumption that sustainable and cost-effective supplies of woody raw material supplies exist in the United States. Wood bioenergy development will also depend on ensuring that wood bioenergy does not have undesirable environmental effects.

The general public's understanding of wood bioenergy is incomplete. Questions swirl around the adequacy of woody biomass supplies in the face of growing demand and evolving policies. A fundamental issue is whether policies should encourage the increased use of biomass through mandates or subsidies. How might mandates affect forest sustainability or distort traditional markets for forest products? In addition, the effect of mandates on the cost of energy to industry and consumers is unknown. These issues vary regionally across the United States and within individual states.

The term *biomass*, when used in the context of energy generation, generally refers to raw material, or *feedstock*, derived biologically from organic sources. Biomass feedstocks are presumed to be renewable: whether obtained from cropland, landfills, forest harvesting, or manufacturing residue, these feedstocks are effectively replenished when crops or trees are replanted and harvested in a sustainable manner.

This book serves as a primer on the role played by wood and American forests in evolving energy markets. It focuses on energy sources that use woody biomass as a feedstock. In the United States, four primary sources produce the biomass supplies of interest to energy producers.

1. Wood from timber harvesting and forest management activities. Timber harvesting (logging) produces industrial roundwood—the logs used to manufacture traditional forest products, such as lumber and paper. Forest thinning and logging operations produce branches, tops, and other non-commercial tree parts, collectively called slash, that cannot be used in standard forest industry manufacturing.

2. Manufacturing residue from forest industry mills. The byproducts of processing roundwood at sawmills include chips, bark, and sawdust.

3. Urban wood waste. Construction and demolition (C&D) debris, yard clippings, wood pallets, and other woody materials disposed from homes, offices, and construction sites are part of the municipal solid waste (MSW) stream that would otherwise go to a landfill.

4. Other forest and tree removals. Trees cleared for real estate development or land conversion can also become biomass for energy production.

WHO SHOULD BE INTERESTED

Evolving wood bioenergy markets interest people in a variety of fields:

- *Energy producers and investors.* This group includes utility company executives, investors in bioenergy projects, and the project developers themselves—the businesses working to build and operate bioenergy projects.

- *Energy consumers.* For both businesses and individuals, the availability, consistency, and cost of electricity and fuel are important.

- *Policymakers.* Local, state, and federal incentives or disincentives for bioenergy projects can determine whether and where developers can build bioenergy plants.

- *Service providers.* Bioenergy projects use the services of forestry consultants, bankers, accountants, lawyers, and the manufacturers of equipment that processes raw material or makes bioenergy products.

- *Wood suppliers and forest owners.* Bioenergy projects represent potential new customers for forest owners.

- *Community leaders and citizens.* Community attitudes can affect project development, depending on whether people anticipate that a bioenergy product will bring new jobs or higher power prices or health and environmental harms.

Energy and wood markets provide mechanisms to allocate resources and allow these parties to work together to serve consumers, support sustainable economic growth, and provide reliable renewable energy. A brief look backward reminds us that the story of shifting energy sources and growing energy needs is older than the United States itself.

CHAPTER ONE

History of Wood Energy in the United States

Woody biomass has generated energy for thousands of years and has enabled us to convert available resources to meet human needs. Even after oils, agricultural wastes, and wind became sources of power, wood remained the most-used energy resource for centuries, and technologies improved to expand its use. In the 1300s, Germans built the first blast furnaces to burn wood at extremely high temperatures, allowing them to produce large quantities of iron. During the next few centuries, much of Europe's forested area was logged for iron production and shipbuilding. As logging started to reduce timber supplies, Europeans became concerned about the supply of wood. The colonization of North America gave Europe access to new forest resources.

Beginning in the colonial period, Americans have benefited from ready access to plentiful forests. In the 1700s, New Englanders' access to wood as fuel allowed for unlimited home heating—a luxury that these settlers could not have replicated in England. The heavy use of wood began to reduce wood supplies. Benjamin Franklin bemoaned the work, travel, and cost required to fetch fuelwood that once had been "at any man's door." In his historical geography *Americans and Their Forests*, Michael Williams describes the proliferation of fuel dealers as the trade in wood developed to meet urban demand. These wood markets required some oversight, and beginning in 1680, New York, Boston, Newport, Philadelphia, and other locales appointed official "corders," whose job was to ensure that fuelwood dealers did not cheat consumers.

In the late 1700s, energy uses consumed two-thirds of the wood removed from forests. As towns grew and demand for fuelwood increased, suppliers traveled farther and farther to reach forests. Winter months could produce critical shortages. Williams summarizes the effects on local markets, noting that wood prices would "quadruple or quintuple to 40 or 50 shillings [per cord], particularly in bad weather." Timber supplies remained abundant, but the price spikes reflected the longer hauling distances from forests to cities.

After 1775, small sloops carrying 25 to 50 cords began shipping wood from a new, plentiful fuel source: the pine barrens of New Jersey. Wood-cutters became increasingly sophisticated and bought forestland, ships, and wharves, becoming (in modern terms) vertically integrated. They also expanded into charcoal burning and pitch extraction. In the colonial period, the average annual per capita use of fuelwood was approximately 4.5 cords, or about half of a log truckload.

In the 1700s and into the 1800s, use of fuelwood, in the form of charcoal, extended beyond the home to industrial purposes. Wood was stacked in teepee fashion, covered with soil, and carefully burned so that the heat would break down the wood into gases, a watery tar mixture called ligno-sulfonic acid, and charcoal. Wood charcoal—which burns hotter than wood, resists insects and decay, and is lighter to transport—was used to produce iron and other metals. The vast majority of iron produced in America throughout the 18th century was smelted using wood charcoal. Small plants produced 300 to 800 tons per year of pig (crude) iron; each ton required 125 to 400 bushels of charcoal.

INDUSTRIAL REVOLUTION

By the 1800s, wood charcoal generated the heat that factories needed for manufacturing. These wood-using industries included breweries and distilleries, iron casting and steel furnaces, and works for salt, potash, and animal and vegetable oils. Using charcoal complemented economic growth because forestland needed to be cleared for agriculture. In *Americans and Their Forests*, Williams notes how the work of clearing forests aligned the values of hard work, frugality, and moral effort. As the economy developed, the growing U.S. population removed forests to accommodate new farms, pastures, cities, industries, and roads.

Wood supported a variety of commercial activities. Manufacturers burned different species of wood, depending on their needs and its availability. For

The stacked wood is ready to be covered with soil and fired. A cord of wood produced 20 to 40 bushels of charcoal; an acre of timberland could yield 1,200 bushels. About 200 bushels were required to smelt 1 ton of pig iron.

example, bakers and brickmakers in New York, Philadelphia, and Baltimore used pitch pine. Hatters in Pittsburg used charcoal made from white (sugar) maple. Salt makers in New York used wood brought from the north and west on the Erie Canal.

Steamboats, constructed from and powered by wood, became the dominant mode of transportation and shipping in the 1800s in the United States. Between the 1810s and the Civil War, the number of steamboats working the Ohio and Mississippi rivers and their navigable tributaries escalated. The steamboats were built along the rivers they plied. Unlike the steampowered ships that crossed the Atlantic and relied on coal, these new steamships burned wood. Both the timbers for shipbuilding and the fuel to power the vessels came from the abundant forests on the river banks.

Steamboats required large volumes of wood for their boilers. To supply the steamboats, thousands of wood yards appeared, where timber was delivered and cut to the correct size for the ship furnaces. The owners of the wood yards kept huge fires burning at night so that the ship crews could know where to stop to refuel.

The establishment of the rail network in America followed a similar path to that of steamboats. In England, locomotives burned coal. However, in the United States up until the Civil War, trains consumed wood and required a network of wood yards and woodsheds along the tracks. Typically, trains stopped every two hours to reload wood for fuel. The networks evolved into systematic operations. For example, operators of the New York Central line constructed and maintained 115 woodsheds. One railroad with a north-south line from Lake Michigan to the Ohio River maintained wood fuel locations—called "wood-up" stations—every 20 to 25 miles.

The increase in wood use to fuel locomotives and steamboats created timberland investment opportunities. Speculators who acquired timberland near potential railroad lines expected to benefit from future demand for their timber assets. The construction and operation of railroads provided plentiful and long-running cash flows and returns for these pioneering timberland owners.

Steamboats relied on wood for their construction and power, but it was railroads that used truly vast quantities of wood—not just for cars and fuel, but for ties, bridges, and station houses as well. By the end of the 19th century, railroads accounted for one-fifth to one-quarter of total U.S. timber consumption.

The Industrial Revolution greatly expanded the applications of wood used for manufacturing and transportation purposes. In addition, wood raw materials were increasingly used for building products, such as lumber. The increase in wood use drove up wood prices. Forests, as a source of fuel, simply could not keep up with the growing demand for energy, and by the 1800s wood resources became increasingly expensive as firms had to travel farther to reach standing forests. Manufacturers then shifted to less expensive coal and petroleum fuels for energy. Plentiful, cheap coal contributed to the transition from wood to coal for energy. This is a common occurrence in energy markets: consumers choose energy sources based on availability and cost, shifting to the most abundant and cost-effective sources at the time.

Wood-fueled locomotives typically stopped every two hours to reload wood for fuel.

The shift from wood to coal and petroleum products accelerated into the first part of the 20th century. The U.S. Department of Energy estimates that as of 1900, wood provided 21 percent of the energy in the United States, while coal use had grown to 70 percent of U.S. energy consumption. By

1950, wood accounted for only 5 percent; coal, petroleum products, and natural gas provided 36 percent, 38 percent, and 17 percent, respectively.

THE 1970s TO THE 2000s

New interest in woody biomass for energy occurred in the United States in the 1970s, following the 1973 oil embargo by the Arab members of the Organization of Petroleum Exporting Countries. The Department of Energy solicited research in 1977 to determine the possibility of wood production for energy. Biomass power plants were built, primarily in the Northeast and California, in response to legislation in the late 1970s that allowed independent producers to sell power to utilities. The forest products industry, especially the pulp and paper sector, continued to use its own wood waste, including bark and chips too small to pulp, to produce the steam, heat, and power required for industrial processes ("process energy"). Wood pellet stoves grew in popularity, especially in the Northeast. Despite the momentum of bioenergy in the 1970s and early 1980s, investment interest receded with the falling oil prices in the mid-1980s (Figure 1.1). Oil price increases following the September 11, 2001, terrorist attacks and U.S.

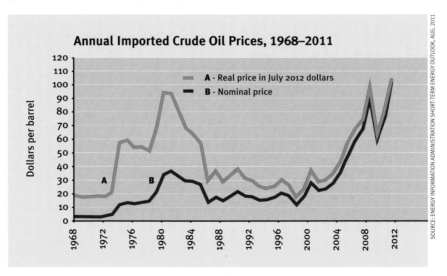

SOURCE: ENERGY INFORMATION ADMINISTRATION SHORT-TERM ENERGY OUTLOOK, AUG. 2011

Figure 1.1. In the 1980s, falling real prices for oil checked investors' interest in bioenergy projects.

military efforts in the Middle East revived the national interest in bioenergy, including bioenergy from woody materials.

Today, sawmills use wood residue to feed boilers that produce heat for drying lumber. Pulp mills combust the wood residue from their manufacturing processes to produce steam and electricity, with the majority producing process heat and steam. Pulp and paper mills also use spent pulping chemicals, or black liquor, to fuel chemical recovery furnaces. For these facilities, investing in the skills and equipment needed to produce energy from wood represented a natural fit and synergy.

The forest products industry leads the United States in energy generation from woody biomass. According to the U.S. Energy Information Administration (EIA), this industry accounts for more than 76 percent of the country's industrial biomass energy consumption and electricity generation. Between 2005 and 2010, estimated wood consumption for energy

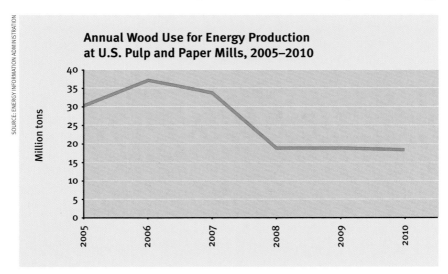

SOURCE: ENERGY INFORMATION ADMINISTRATION

Figure 1.2. Lumber, paper, and other forest products account for 76.7 percent of the 1.966 trillion Btu of biomass energy consumption. Wood consumption for energy production at pulp and paper facilities declined after 2007 for several reasons: demand for pulp and paper fell during the economic recession, severe declines in sawmill production and forest logging reduced the supplies of feedstock, and a 45.5 percent decline in natural gas prices between 2008 and 2009 gave industrial facilities a cheap alternative.

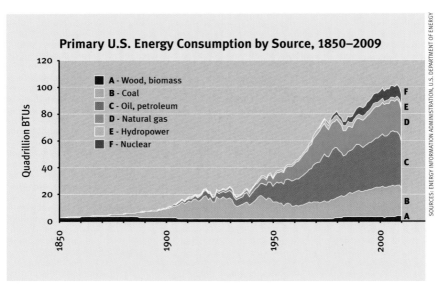

Figure 1.3. In 1850, wood accounted for nearly 91 percent of U.S. energy use. Since then, energy use has grown nearly 3,900 percent, with fossil fuels (coal, petroleum, and natural gas) accounting for 84 percent and wood and other biomass accounting for just over 4 percent.

production at U.S. pulp and paper mills ranged from 19.2 million to 36.0 million tons per year (Figure 1.2). The decline in these mills' wood use for energy between 2007 and 2010 reflects the economic recession and a period of low natural gas prices.

Renewable power alternatives continue to gain prominence in the United States. This stems from a sense of urgency fueled by high gas prices, legislative actions associated with greenhouse gas (GHG) emissions from fossil fuels, and national security concerns about the proportion of imported petroleum (approximately 70 percent of U.S. supply). In addition, energy consumption continues to grow in the United States, both per person and in total. According to EIA, per capita energy use increased 44 percent between 1949 and 2009. In 2010, renewable energy accounted for about 8 percent of total U.S. energy use, just below that provided by nuclear energy facilities in 2009. Energy from wood and biomass constituted 4.2 percent of U.S. energy use in 2009 (Figure 1.3).

Cars formed long lines during the 1973 oil embargo by the Arab members of the Organization of Petroleum Exporting Countries. Initially targeting the United States for its support of Israel during the Yom Kippur War, the embargo lasted five months before being lifted in 1974 and created interest in bioenergy.

The U.S. forest products industry has long consumed woody biomass for energy. Now other opportunities have attracted the attention of investors, policymakers, and communities looking to increase the production of renewable energy. Some of these opportunities are efforts to develop cutting-edge technologies or modify coal-burning power plants. Many projects, however, build on well-understood processes to turn wood into an easily transported and consumed energy product: wood pellets.

CHAPTER TWO

Wood Pellets

W ood pellets are small cylinders of compressed dry sawdust, wood shavings, or wood chips; they measure 6–10 mm by 10–30 mm, or about the thickness of a pencil and an inch long. Because the compacted biomass has a low moisture content, pellets store well and can be transported easily. They are used in pellet stoves— thermostat-controlled woodstoves with automated feeders.

In raw form, wood has low energy density, which is the amount of energy per unit of weight. Since water makes up half the weight of wood, half of the expense associated with transporting wood goes to handling water. Although forest industry facilities prefer green wood, which contains water, it takes more energy to burn wet wood than dry wood. Pelletizing wood addresses these issues by increasing the energy content per unit volume to near that of coal and dropping the moisture content from near 50 percent in raw wood to less than 10 percent.

Making wood pellets involves grinding, compressing, shaping, cooling, and screening. In a pellet-making facility, hammer mills pound wood into sawdust. Sometimes drying further reduces moisture content at this stage. The sawdust is then sent to a pelleting machine, where it is subjected to high pressure and extruded through a die to take shape. The consistency and uniformity of wood pellets, which combust readily, make them well suited for pellet stoves.

Pellet grades depend on how they will be used. "Premium" pellets have lower ash content (less than 1 percent) than other pellet grades and represent approximately 95 percent of current pellet production. These are

Wood pellets are cofired with coal in pulverized-coal furnaces to generate electricity. Wood pellet stoves for residential use have automated feeders and can be controlled with a thermostat.

preferred for residential uses in stoves and furnaces. "Standard" pellets contain up to 3 percent ash content and are used for industrial applications.

Pellets have drawbacks. Moisture absorption can be a problem and should be considered during transportation and storage. Another concern with pellet production and storage is superheating and off-gassing. Pellets are stored in piles and over time the temperature of the pellets rises in the center of the pile; this increase in temperature can cause the piles to spontaneously combust. As the piles become hot, the pellets also emit volatile organic compounds. Dust production represents a health hazard associated with pellet production. Pellet facilities must install specialized systems to control dust and aerate pellet piles to prevent heating and combustion.

The pellet concept originated in the United States, but the initial form took a different shape. In 1930, the Potlatch pine sawmill in Lewiston, Idaho, began making what it called the Pres-to-Log, an artificial fuel for wood-burning stoves. Developed to recycle sawdust and wood shavings, the Pres-to-Log process mirrored that for modern pellets but, as its name suggests, resulted in a log form.

USES OF WOOD PELLETS

Wood pellets have two primary uses: producing heat in homes and producing electricity for power. At power plants, pellets can be cofired with coal in pulverized coal furnaces to generate electricity. Cofiring mixes wood with coal in the same combustion chamber. The percentage of the wood mixed with coal varies based on the combustion system and the objectives of the firm.

Increased demand for pellets in the United States has been associated with disruptions in oil supplies, high oil prices, and most recently, environmental concerns. Wood pellets were introduced in North America in the 1970s as an alternative fuel in response to the oil embargo and energy crisis of 1973 and were used mainly by industrial, commercial, and institutional sectors for heating. Thereafter, demand increased for pelletized fuel for stokers, a boiler type used to produce steam. Pellet supplies were unreliable, however, and once oil prices began to fall after the embargo ended, wood pellet consumption by industrial users stagnated.

Historically, most U.S. pellet production fed the domestic, home-heating market. More than 800,000 U.S. homes use wood pellets for heat. Pellets

TORREFIED BIOMASS

Torrefied biomass is similar to wood pellets but is designed for cofiring with coal. Regular pellets cannot be pulverized in a coal-burning plant because they break down into sawdust, which flows inefficiently. The torrefaction process is a slow thermochemical treatment at temperatures between 200° and 300°C (392° to 572°F). This process gives the wood coal-like properties, making it easier to pulverize with coal in a coal-burning plant. Torrefied biomass also repels water—an advantage over wood pellets, which must be kept dry during transport and storage. Although torrefied biomass has promise for cofiring applications, the technology remains in development. It has been proven at pilot scale, in the lab, but has not been successfully demonstrated in a commercial-scale plant. In addition, torrefaction emits organic compounds and produces tar—undesirable by-products that require further processing.

PHOTO COURTESY OF CATE STREET CAPITAL, INC.

Torrefied "roasted" biomass is dense enough that it can be cofired with coal, but the technology is still in development.

are packaged in easily transported 40-pound bags. The Northeast and North Central states lead the country in pellet production. According to Spelter and Toth at the U.S. Forest Service (2009), the average home with a pellet stove consumes about 2 tons per year. Homes in the middle or northern United States that rely exclusively on pellet stoves for heat may use about 4 tons of pellets per year; however, most pellet stoves supplement other heating systems or are only used occasionally in homes in milder climates.

While use of wood pellets in U.S. homes has increased, purchases of fireplaces and wood-burning stoves have declined. Shipments of fireplaces and woodstoves fell by about 65 percent between 1998 and 2010, with the steepest decline corresponding to the decline in the U.S. housing market, beginning in 2005. Over the same period, U.S. shipments of wood pellet stoves increased by 30 percent, sometimes exceeding 100,000 units per year (Figure 2.1). The rising number of wood pellet stoves shipped during a depressed housing market implies a dramatic shift in consumer preferences and a renewed interest in the potential of wood-based heat for meeting household needs.

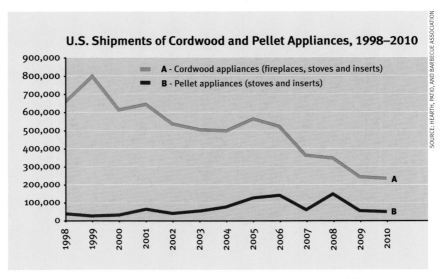

Figure 2.1. Shipments of fireplaces and traditional wood stoves fell 64.6 percent between 1998 and 2010, but shipments of wood pellet stoves increased 30.2 percent over the same period, exceeding 100,000 units three times in four years.

SNAPSHOT OF U.S. PELLET PRODUCTION

As of June 2012, there were 116 pellet plants operating in the United States, 5 plants under construction, and 44 in the planning stages, according to Forisk Consulting. Regionally, the North leads the United States with the most pellet plants operating. The capacity for pellet production has increased dramatically in the United States since 2008. The United States produced 2 million tons of pellets as of 2008, about 66 percent of the industry's capacity to produce pellets. Canada produced 1.5 million tons of pellets in 2008, which was 81 percent of that nation's capacity. By 2011, pellet capacity in the United States totaled 7.7 million tons, nearly trebling the capacity of 2008. Pellet capacity in the United States could exceed 9.4 million tons by 2012 if all announced projects open.

By comparison, Europe in 2008 consumed over 8 million tons of pellets, led by Sweden, Denmark, the Netherlands, Belgium, and Italy. Sweden has been the world's largest producer and consumer, having used 2.1 million tons of pellets in 2008 alone. The European Union (EU) seeks to supply 20 percent of its energy needs from renewable sources by 2020. As of 2006, EU renewable energy use was 9.2 percent of total energy use. Thus, the EU will have to increase its renewable energy percentage from 9.2 percent to 20 percent in 14 years. Europe's growing demand for and consumption of wood pellets have encouraged investments in pellet production capacity. As a result, European firms looked abroad, primarily to North America, as an alternative wood pellet source. Russia is also increasing its capacity to produce pellets.

Meanwhile, global wood pellet markets continue to grow, largely in response to EU mandates. Pellet production increased from 8 million tons per year in 2007 to more than 13 million tons in 2009. Currently, Europe consumes most of this production.

Pellet capacity in the United States is expected to exceed 15.6 million tons per year by 2016, doubling the capacity from 2011 (Figure 2.2). The largest capacity increases based on known projects would occur in the South, which could nearly triple pellet capacity over this period. Most newly announced pellet projects look to serve the European market.

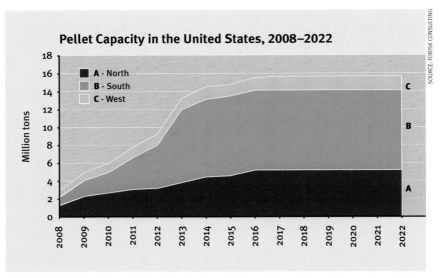

Figure 2.2. Pellet capacity in the United States is expected to exceed 15.6 million tons per year by 2016. The largest increases occur in the South, where capacity may nearly triple. Most newly announced pellet projects intend to serve the European market.

WOOD PELLET RAW MATERIALS

Historically in Canada and the United States, raw material feedstocks for wood pellets were primarily manufacturing mill residue; roundwood pulpwood and in-woods chips (raw material trucked directly from the forest) were secondary sources. High dependence on sawmill residue means that when sawmills produce less lumber, as they do when housing markets decline, the pellet mills cannot find sufficient supplies of the raw material they need. For this reason, most of the feedstock volume for new plants will come from roundwood chipped on-site or in the woods instead of from mill residue. These new export-oriented pellet facilities are larger than traditional pellet mills and need to reduce the risk associated with supply availability. The ability to procure and process roundwood and logging residue gives pellet mills more control over supply because they can use raw materials that are not subject to lumber and housing markets (Figure 2.3).

Municipal sources, such as construction and demolition materials (C&D) and waste wood, are generally unimportant to pellet plants. Currently, these

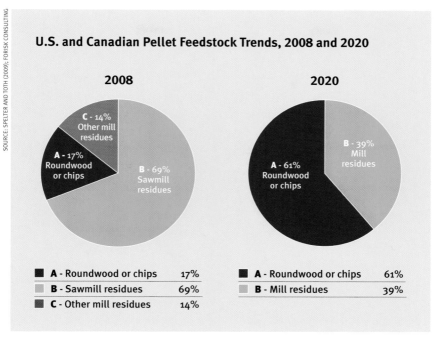

Figure 2.3. Historically in North America, wood pellet raw materials were primarily manufacturing residue and secondarily pulpwood and in-woods chips (raw material trucked directly from the forest), according to research by the U.S. Forest Service. Now, most pellet feedstocks are nonmill residue, primarily roundwood chipped on-site or in the woods. Large pellet facilities procure and process their own feedstock so that they can manage quality and ensure supply.

sources are inconsistent and entail costs associated with removing nails and other metals. Pellet plants also cannot use raw materials contaminated with chemicals or paint. Some pellet mills do supplement their core wood raw materials with clean urban waste, such as pallets.

FUTURE OF U.S. WOOD PELLET MARKETS

In 2008, more than 80 percent of U.S. pellet production was shipped domestically, with most of the balance shipped to markets in Europe. Overall, pellet exports from the United States are relatively modest (Figure 2.4). Canada has long been the dominant exporter of wood pellets to Europe, but the United States has recently and aggressively increased its export

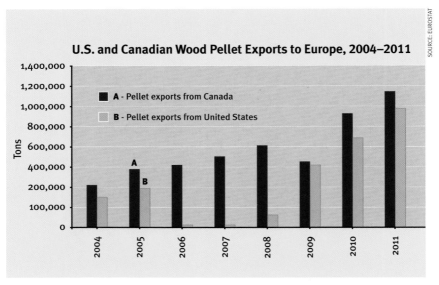

Figure 2.4. Canada has long been the dominant exporter of pellets to Europe, but volumes from the United States have recently increased. These exports include sawdust, wood waste, and briquettes as well as wood pellets.

volumes in response to demand abroad. Several large biomass power projects being developed in Europe plan to import substantial portions of their wood fiber. The European Union's goal of supplying 20 percent of its energy needs from renewable sources by 2020 has increased worldwide pellet demand. In addition, the market for wood pellets grew after the Kyoto Protocol, signed in 1997, took effect in 2005 and set binding targets for 37 industrialized countries to reduce greenhouse gas emissions. To meet domestic needs and expand supplies, European firms look to Canada and the United States as potential sources of pellets.

Some argue that exporting wood pellets from the United States to Europe transfers pressure on European forests to those of the United States. Others welcome European financing and investment in U.S. markets as a way to create manufacturing jobs. The conflicting views associated with wood pellet exports to Europe echo concerns from hundreds of years ago when America was still one of England's colonies. In the 1600s several English writers wanted to transfer the iron industry from England to America to relieve pressure on English forests. In 1609, one pamphleteer wrote that "woods across the Atlantic would be devoured instead of trees in England." Today's European interest in American forests once again raises questions about sustainability.

Forest certification is a mechanism to prevent unsustainable timber harvesting and to dispel fears of European exploitation of American forests. Third-party certification programs guarantee sustainable forest management based on a standard set of criteria. European customers today prefer pellets made from certified wood grown in forests enrolled in certification programs as proof that they are not depleting forests in America. Forest certification programs include the Sustainable Forestry Initiative (SFI), Forest Stewardship Council (FSC), and American Tree Farm System (ATFS). SFI is a program preferred by industrial timberland owners in the United States. In 2005, the Programme for the Endorsement of Forest Certification (PEFC) endorsed SFI, giving it international recognition. The Forest Stewardship Council (FSC), based in Oaxaca, Mexico, is a major international certifier and a competitor of SFI. The American Tree Farm System (ATFS), the oldest and largest woodland system in the U.S., has long focused on certifying nonindustrial family forest owners in addition to industrial forestlands. Many European pellet customers would also like their pellet suppliers to be certified by the international Green Gold Label, which is specific to biomass; it provides chain-of-custody certification encompassing the entire pellet process, from raw material to processing, transport, and energy production.

The future of wood pellet use in the United States may depend on efforts to reduce carbon dioxide (CO_2) emissions. Coal-burning plants, the prime target of CO_2 reductions, produce more than half of U.S. electricity. Greenhouse gas mitigation efforts will increase demand for coal substitutes or complements. In addition, wood pellet use in U.S. homes has significant room to grow. Pellets can often be used where firewood is banned because they burn more efficiently than firewood.

As the sector grows, access to manufacturing residue will shrink and new facilities will turn increasingly to roundwood for their raw material to satisfy export contracts for European consumers. The possibility that electricity-generating plants in the United States will be required to obtain a portion of their feedstock from biomass could influence current wood biomass flows and change the competitive landscape for wood raw materials.

CHAPTER THREE

Wood for Electricity

Understanding the changing role of wood in electrical power generation requires a familiarity with how federal policies have shaped the electricity industry in the United States. Prior to 1935, large utilities were basically unregulated. In 1935, the Public Utility Holding Company Act (PUHCA) was enacted to protect the public from high electricity costs and large holding companies that controlled the electricity distribution networks. PUHCA authorized the Securities and Exchange Commission to oversee electric utilities and restricted the geographical area in which each could operate. Still, only utilities could produce electricity for sale.

In 1978, in response to the oil embargo of 1973 and overall rising prices, the Public Utility Regulatory Policies Act (PURPA) promoted energy efficiency and renewable energy. PURPA required utilities to purchase power from "qualified facilities," small power plants (less than 80 megawatts [MW]) that produced electricity from renewable sources or cogeneration. PURPA established two new electric-producing entities: small power producers and cogenerators (facilities that produce both electricity and steam for heat or power). Prior to PURPA, only utilities could produce electricity for sale; PURPA thus created a market for independent power producers and for power generated from sources such as wood. The utilities were required to purchase power at their "avoided cost of production," the cost that the utility would have to pay to produce the renewable energy themselves. Many power purchase agreements between utilities and independent power producers initiated by PURPA in the 1980s are coming up for renewal in the 2000s.

The Energy Policy Act of 1992 allowed wholesale electricity producers to access the national electricity transmission system. Nonutility electricity producers could now sell electricity directly to the grid. This market access is critical to independent power producers who develop renewable energy projects.

Legislative proposals for a national renewable energy standard (RES) would require electric utilities to produce a percentage of their electricity from renewable sources. As of January 2012, the United States did not have a federal standard for renewable energy, but more than half the states have renewable portfolio standards, which require that a certain percentage of the state's electricity come from renewable sources (Figure 3.1). This has

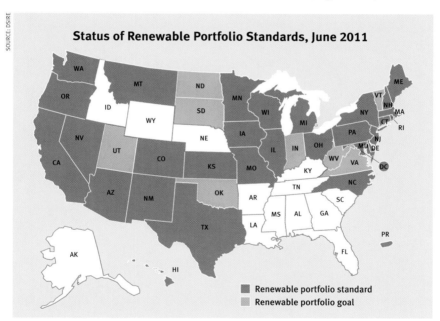

Figure 3.1. Many proposed wood-to-electricity projects are associated with state-level renewable portfolio standards, which require a certain percentage of the electricity generated in a state to come from renewable sources. Southern states have been slow to adopt such standards because politicians and utilities do not want to raise these states' low electricity rates by mandating renewable energy. In addition, utilities make little net revenue selling renewable energy generated by another power producer.

supported growth and interest in investing in and expanding the wood-to-electricity industry.

U.S. ELECTRICITY-GENERATING SOURCES

In 2011, coal fueled 44 percent of the electricity generated in the United States (Figure 3.2), followed by natural gas (25 percent) and nuclear (19 percent). Wood and other minor sources accounted for 6 percent of the electricity generated in 2011.

The vast majority of the electricity used in the United States—over 90 percent—is generated from fossil fuels, nuclear power, or hydropower. But wood is also used to generate power by institutional, commercial, and industrial facilities, such as schools, hospitals, and factories. In fact, these sectors used 70 percent of the wood biomass electricity generated in 2010, while the electric power sector used 30 percent.

Biopower plants burn organic waste, such as wood manufacturing residue, to generate steam that turns electric generators. As of June 2012, 339 wood biopower plants were in development or operating in the United States, according to Forisk Consulting. Of these, 148 are stand-alone power plants or cofiring plants, and 186 are or will be cogeneration plants, primarily located at forest industry mills. Most of the operating stand-alone plants are located in the northern United States and tend to be smaller, averaging 25–30 MW, than the newly announced projects in other regions, which average 60 MW. The largest projects include coal plant conversions, cofires at utilities, and projects planned by independent power producers.

The supply of electricity relies on a combination of base-load and peak-load plants. Base-load plants provide the minimum supply and operate at high capacity, typically 70 percent or more, with low operating costs. These large plants often use coal or nuclear power to reduce costs through economies of scale. Peak-load plants generate electricity at times of high demand; they are typically smaller and rely on natural gas or oil, which is more costly. The use of wood biomass as a source of renewable electricity fits the requirements for base-load plants: biomass feedstock can be procured and inventoried to operate plants continuously, as opposed to solar and wind power—two types of renewable energy that are intermittent.

Wood-to-electricity projects face challenges, however. Because the energy value of coal is higher than that generated from a common unit of wood,

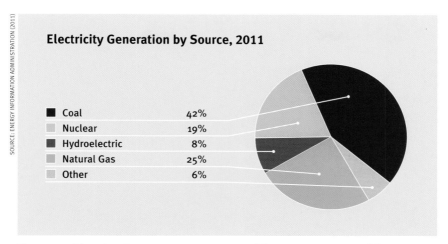

SOURCE: ENERGY INFORMATION ADMINISTRATION (2011)

Electricity Generation by Source, 2011

Coal	42%
Nuclear	19%
Hydroelectric	8%
Natural Gas	25%
Other	6%

Figure 3.2. The electric power sector accounted for over 90 percent of the electricity generated by fossil fuels, nuclear, and hydroelectric sources in 2011. Commercial and industrial sectors (schools, hospitals, factories) used 70 percent of the wood biomass electricity generated in 2010.

high volumes of wood biomass must be delivered, necessitating a sophisticated logistic system. Also, coal plants feature better economies of scale. Wood biomass power plants are smaller than coal plants and thus less cost-efficient; for example, a typical wood bioenergy plant may be 25 to 50 MW, whereas a typical coal plant generates 500 MW or more. In addition, biomass power plants have higher variable costs per unit; for example, a coal plant may average 0.5 cents per kilowatt hour in variable operating costs but a biomass plant may average 0.7 cents per kilowatt hour. According to research from the Massachusetts Institute of Technology, the estimated cost of electricity and transmission for a biomass power plant is 9.1 cents per kilowatt hour, versus 6.1 cents per kilowatt hour for coal.

APPROACHES TO PRODUCING ELECTRICITY FROM WOOD

Electricity can be produced from wood in three ways: direct combustion, particularly cofiring with coal; gasification; and cogeneration, or combined heat and power (CHP).

Direct combustion, the most common method for biomass power plants operating today, burns biomass fuel in a boiler to produce high-pressure steam. This steam turns a turbine and produces electricity. Several types of

HOW TO TRACK ANNOUNCED BIOENERGY PROJECTS

Bioenergy projects must run a gauntlet of activities, from locating a site and securing financing and permits to constructing the plant and procuring raw material. Progress in these specific activities provides a way to determine the viability of bioenergy markets at the local level and allows forest industry professionals and investors to determine the potential effects on wood use and timber markets.

In 2008, Forisk initiated research into tracking U.S. bioenergy projects to quantify the progress of wood bioenergy markets. Screening bioenergy projects is important because assessments that assume all projects succeed overstate likely wood use for energy. There are two questions to ask. First, does the project rely on proven technology? Proven technologies include pelletizing and boilers; cellulosic ethanol from wood feedstock is still evolving. Second, has this project secured at least two of the necessary resources, permits, or agreements? These include financing; air quality permits; engineering, procurement, and construction contracts; power purchase agreements for electricity facilities; interconnection agreements for electricity facilities; and raw material supply agreements.

Other considerations include the actual raw material mix needed by the project, the estimated wood-to-energy conversions, the economic effects of mandates and subsidies, and the stages and timing of each project. Following are the stages of development, along with definitions.

Site selection. A company determines where to locate its plant. This can involve negotiations with landowners to purchase land for a site or with owners of an existing facility to renovate.

Feasibility study. A study assesses the availability and sustainability of raw material supplies at the selected site. The study can include estimated project costs and budgets.

Financing. Raising capital to build and operate a facility can include obtaining public grants or private investment.

Permitting and contracts. This category includes air quality permits, engineering and construction contracts, power purchase agreements for electricity facilities, interconnection agreements for electricity facilities, and wood supply agreements.

...continued from previous page

Construction. Groundbreaking has occurred and construction is underway.

Operating. The facility is purchasing feedstock and generating electricity or producing pellets or liquid fuel.

Distinguishing projects that are likely to happen from projects that are more speculative helps mill managers identify sources of raw material competition while supporting forest owners' efforts to find viable new markets for their wood fiber.

boilers use direct combustion, including furnaces, pile burners, stoker grate boilers, suspension boilers, fluidized bed combustors, and cofiring in coal-fired boilers.

Cofiring involves substituting biomass for a portion of coal in an existing power plant furnace. It is the most economic near-term option for introducing new biomass power generation. Cofiring wood with coal provides several logistic and economic advantages. First, mixing wood with coal can avoid some emissions of nitrogen oxide (NO_x), sulfur oxide (SO_x), and related compounds. Second, the use of cofiring does not require the building of new plants. The primary new investment involves adding wood-handling equipment to an existing coal plant. Third, because the volumes of wood tend to be small, the plant can reduce hauling costs by procuring wood near the plant. However, the typical wood chips produced by the forest products industry are too large and fibrous to pass through coal pulverizers and burn cleanly; the biomass must be small to begin with or converted into wood pellets for cofiring with coal. Also, combusting wood produces SO_x and NO_x, although emissions are lower for wood than for coal.

In gasification, wood biomass is heated in an oxygen-limited environment until it breaks down into a flammable gas. The gas can be used in combined-cycle power generation systems, which combine gas turbines and steam turbines to produce electricity. The efficiency of these systems can reach 60 percent.

Cogeneration produces heat and electricity from a single fuel. The heat can be used in industrial processes; common examples include the pulp and paper process and sawmilling processes. CHP plants are typically located at the point of energy consumption. Biomass heating plants also exist, although in the United States they are small and usually provide heat to dry lumber at sawmills or heat for schools. CHP plants are more efficient than stand-alone biomass electricity plants. For example, a 5-MW CHP plant can have a total efficiency of 75 percent (thermal efficiency of 50 percent and electricity efficiency of 25 percent) compared with a total efficiency of 35 percent for a 50-MW stand-alone biomass power plant.

FUTURE OF WOOD TO ELECTRICITY

The wood-to-electricity market in the United States continues to develop, even though the cost to produce electricity from biomass currently exceeds the cost to produce electricity from coal and natural gas. The reason to use wood at electricity-generating plants is that wood is carbon neutral and therefore a cleaner, greener fuel for electricity than coal (see sidebar in Chapter 6 for a discussion of carbon neutrality). Development depends on state renewable portfolio standards and a possible federal renewable electricity standard. Without political mandates, however, it remains unlikely that the wood-to-electricity market will be competitive, especially in states that lack renewable portfolio standards.

CHAPTER FOUR

Cellulosic Ethanol and Other Wood Liquid Fuels

Producing liquid transportation fuel from trees, grasses, and algae—biofuel—is not yet cost-effective. Despite the technological challenges, dozens of firms are pursuing projects in the United States to produce biofuel from these raw materials. Understanding the history of this sector means revisiting the growth of ethanol production in the United States.

Ethanol, a gasoline fuel additive, is typically produced from starches in corn, sorghum, and sugar cane. Most of the ethanol produced in North America today is derived from corn. Ethanol can also be produced from cellulose, a component of plant cell walls. It is more difficult to break down cellulose and convert it to the sugars needed to make ethanol than to make ethanol from starch.

During the oil price shocks in the early 1970s, ethanol became a way to extend the volume of gasoline. However, a large-scale bioprocessing industry awaited a series of legislative moves and economic incentives. David Mousdale, in *Introduction to Biofuels*, highlights three federal environmental regulations. First, the 1970 Clean Air Act created the requirement for cleaner-burning gasoline and ultimately the mandatory inclusion of oxygenates, or oxygen-rich additives. Second, the 1988 Alternative Motor Fuels Act promoted and advanced the development of ethanol and other alternative fuels by creating incentives in the form of Corporate Average Fuel Economy (CAFE) credits for manufacturers that produced motor vehicles capable of operating on certain alternative fuels. Third, the 1992 Energy Policy Act mandated that the federal government's vehicle fleet include

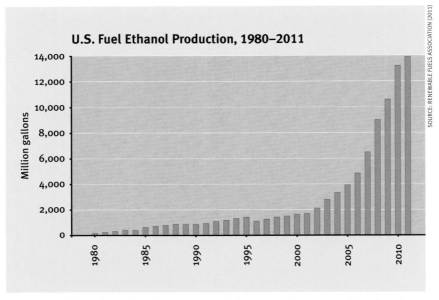

Figure 4.1. Ethanol has long been a candidate oxygenate for gasoline, but the Environmental Protection Agency first approved methyl tertiary butyl ether (MTBE), a product of the petrochemical industry. In 1999, reports surfaced of environmental pollution caused by MTBE spills (Mousdale 2010), and in 2002, states began banning the substance. Corn-based ethanol filled the vacuum. After a decade of minimal growth in the 1990s, ethanol production increased rapidly.

increasing numbers of vehicles powered by domestically produced alternative fuels, such as ethanol.

Beginning in 2005, ethanol use increased sharply in the United States as it replaced methyl tertiary butyl ether (more familiarly known as MTBE), an oxygenate and gasoline additive (Figure 4.1). Although the costs of ethanol production have declined over time, it remains cost prohibitive especially when corn prices rise. This is especially true with cellulosic ethanol made from wood, which requires major advances in pretreatment and fermentation processes of the feedstock to be competitive with gasoline.

In 2005, the United States had become the largest ethanol-producing nation, supplanting Brazil. The 2005 Energy Policy Act created a renewable fuels standard expected to increase the use of renewable fuels from 4 billion

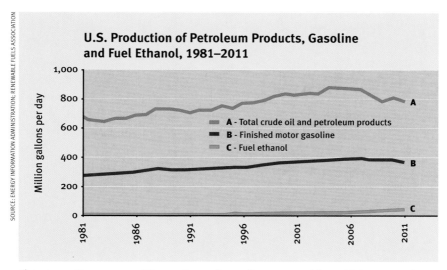

Figure 4.2. Some 370 million gallons of gasoline are used by vehicles every day in the United States. Fuel ethanol, an alcohol fuel made from corn and other renewable sources of biomass, represents another 38 million gallons per day (10 percent) to U.S. markets. To date, fuel ethanol accounts for a small but growing source of renewable transport fuel for U.S. consumers.

gallons in 2006 to 7.5 billion gallons in 2012, mostly in fuel derived from corn. In 2011, fuel ethanol represented a 10 percent addition to the U.S. motor gasoline markets. To date, fuel ethanol accounts for a small but growing source of renewable transport fuel for U.S. consumers (Figure 4.2).

CELLULOSIC VERSUS CORN ETHANOL

Cellulosic ethanol neatly sidesteps a key issue associated with corn ethanol: corn ethanol competes with corn demand for human consumption and can raise the price of food and feed. Although the sweet corn grown for human use differs from the feed corn grown for animals and ethanol, the decision of which type to plant is driven by profitability to farmers. Cellulosic ethanol eliminates the problem of using a fuel source that competes with a food source.

Whether derived from cornstarch or from cellulose, ethanol is less efficient, delivering fewer miles to the gallon than gasoline. Also, as an additive, it does not stand on its own as a drop-in fuel that consumers can pump directly into their cars. Other technologies that could directly substitute for gasoline and produce drop-in fuels from wood and other cellulosic sources are attractive for these reasons. Like cellulosic ethanol, technologies to produce drop-in fuels from cellulose remain in development and currently unproven at commercial scale. However, the case for cellulosic ethanol and other wood-derived biofuels continues to thrive on five arguments:

- Fossil fuel energy sources are limited, and depletion of these resources is more a question of when than if.
- Wood raw material sources are renewable.
- Wood biofuels reduce dependency on petroleum imports.
- Wood biofuels support efforts to encourage sustainable development through new industries for developing nations and more environmentally benign energy production in fast-growing economies such as China and India.
- The use and production of wood biofuels seem to support efforts to mitigate global CO_2 emissions.

DEVELOPMENT OF CELLULOSIC ETHANOL TECHNOLOGY

Whereas corn ethanol projects face criticism, cellulosic fuel projects have generated enthusiasm. Dozens of projects have been announced in the United States, yet it remains unclear when cellulosic ethanol and related wood-based transportation fuels will prove technologically feasible and economically competitive. Investors, policymakers, and consumers have an interest in better understanding the commercialization of cellulosic ethanol.

Advanced wood-based biofuels, including ethanol and drop-in alternatives, face multiple challenges. For example, financing has been scarce in the United States since 2009, leading to high dependence on government-guaranteed debt. In addition, to satisfy renewable fuel standards, cellulosic ethanol projects must have low greenhouse gas emissions. The "blend-wall"—the allowable volume of ethanol by percentage that can be mixed with gasoline—is another hurdle. Currently, E10 (10 percent ethanol, 90 percent gasoline) is the standard blend of gasoline used in the United States. In January 2011, the Environmental Protection Agency (EPA) approved a waiver for model year 2001–2006 vehicles to use E15 (15 percent ethanol). As of November 2011, E15 had not been registered with the EPA and was not legal for sale as a transportation fuel in standard gasoline

FINANCING BIOENERGY PROJECTS

Financing represents a special challenge for bioenergy plants, which must compete with other bioenergy projects as well as projects of all types in different industries. The ability to secure financing from a lender indicates some level of confidence and manageable risk in the eyes of the investors.

Wood bioenergy projects rely on at least five sources of financing:

Private equity comes from investors, hedge funds, or private equity firms, whose direct investments represent ownership stakes in the projects.

Grants are available from federal or state agencies. For example, the U.S. Department of Energy (DOE) funds four types of financial assistance through its Office of Energy Efficiency and Renewable Energy: grants, cooperative agreements, continuation awards, and renewable awards. Grants are the most common and are awarded on a competitive basis.

Project financing provides "nonrecourse" loans to specific projects. Payment of debts is backed solely by the assets and revenues from the project. If the project fails to generate revenues sufficient to service the debt and cover expenses, the lender's only recourse is to pursue the assets and revenues of the project, not those of the investors. For this reason, project finance often requires more due diligence and complex contracts.

Loans may be available from banks, private equity firms, or development authorities. Private loans are sometimes guaranteed by public agencies, such as the Rural Utilities Service of the U.S. Department of Agriculture (USDA). DOE's Loan Programs Office oversees three loan programs: (1) the Section 1703 program, which supports the deployment of innovative technologies that avoid, reduce, or sequester greenhouse gas emissions; (2) the Section 1705 program, which was created by the American Reinvestment and Recovery Act of 2009 to support energy projects having difficulties raising financing in tight credit markets; and (3) the Advanced Technology Vehicles Manufacturing Program, which provides direct loans for development of vehicle technologies.

Bonds are issued specifically to finance a given project, and the income can be tax-free. For example, the Clean Renewable Energy Bonds derived from the Energy Tax Incentive Act of 2005 authorized up to $800 million in tax credit bonds for certain kinds of projects.

pumps. Flex-fuel vehicles, meanwhile, can use blends up to E85 (85 percent ethanol) dispensed from pumps labeled for flex-fuel vehicles. If an increase in flex-fuel vehicle purchases increases the market's appetite for E85, which is not yet readily available in the United States, gas stations would have to respond with new pump infrastructure.

As of June 2012, cellulosic ethanol or related fuels are not being produced economically at commercial scale. Production costs are too high. The primary challenge remains the efficient breakdown of cellulose, a focus of bioenergy lab research. In 2011, Forisk Consulting and the Schiamberg Group evaluated 12 liquid fuel wood bioenergy technologies being used to convert wood to transportation fuels, including ethanol, butanol, diesel, gasoline, and jet fuel. Each technology was evaluated for its level of technical risk, potential timeline for commercialization, and expected yields at commercial scale. The results indicated that major technical hurdles remain unsolved and will delay or disrupt commercialization. Figure 4.3 shows the location and relative size of 40 publicly announced projects under construction in the United States.

There are three categories of production plants, by size:
- Commercial scale uses at least 1,400 green tons of feedstock per day to produce at least 10 million to 20 million gallons of biofuel per year.
- Demonstration scale uses approximately 140 green tons of feedstock per day and produces at least 1 million gallons of biofuel per year.
- Pilot scale is generally smaller and used to develop new methods and technologies.

As of June 2012, more than 70 percent of the commercial-scale projects remained in the planning stages. No commercial-scale projects were operating or could claim any level of production. In addition, no demonstration-scale projects were operating, and two-thirds of them remained in the planning stages. In short, the sector is characterized by lots of pilot or test-scale operations and the absence of commercial-scale operations.

PROCESSES USED TO CONVERT WOOD TO BIOFUELS

Three general methods are used to convert wood to biofuels: gasification, hydrolysis and fermentation, and pyrolysis (Figure 4.4). The gasification method heats wood with limited amounts of oxygen or steam and produces

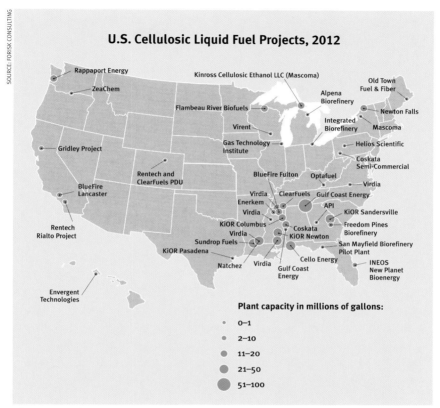

Figure 4.3. The map shows announced liquid fuel projects through June 2012. Projects are in various stages of development, including some that have stalled. Of the 40 biofuel projects planning to use wood in the United States, none can yet economically produce liquid fuels at scale. Note: Virdia plans to produce refined sugars and lignin for a variety of applications, including chemicals and fuels. Virdia's capacity is shown as gallons of output based on the amount of wood they may use relative to other plants.

a synthesis gas. This "syngas" is further processed into ethanol or diesel fuels. Hydrolysis and fermentation break down cellulose and hemicellulose fibers into their component sugars, which are fermented into ethanol. Pyrolysis exposes wood to high heat in the absence of oxygen to form bio-oil, which is processed to form liquid fuels like diesel or gasoline.

Routes for Conversion of Wood to Transportation Fuel

SOURCE: MENDELL, ET AL. (2011)

	PROCESS FLOW		
Gasification	Wood ⇒	syngas ⇒	ethanol, diesel
Hydrolysis and fermentation	Wood ⇒	sugar ⇒	ethanol, butanol
Pyrolysis	Wood ⇒	bio oil ⇒	diesel, gasoline

Figure 4.4. There are three general pathways to convert wood to transporation fuel: gasification, hydrolysis and fermentation, and pyrolysis.

When any raw material is converted to ethanol, some energy is lost. Energy efficiency is a measure of the energy needed to produce the fuel compared with the energy value of the end product. A 2005 study found that the energy input to convert wood to ethanol was 57 percent higher than the energy content of the ethanol itself. Other research, however, indicates the potential for net positive energy gains from biomass-derived fuels. According to Kevin Bullis of *Technology Review*, for cellulosic ethanol, the ratio of the amount of energy in the liquid fuel product to the amount of energy required to produce the liquid fuel product is around 4.4 to 6.1. That is, the cellulosic ethanol contains 440 to 610 percent more energy than is required to produce it. Further study is needed to evaluate the true energy efficiency of wood transportation fuels.

WOOD USE FOR BIOFUEL PRODUCTION

Timberland owners view biofuel plants as potential markets for wood grown in their forests. On a national scale, however, the sector has limited potential for significantly expanding wood markets. If successful, existing biofuel projects would consume less than 18 million tons of wood per year by 2030. In comparison, the U.S. forest products industry consumes more than 500 million tons of wood annually.

Increasingly, investors are asking how else they might profit from wood-based ethanol projects. Several companies have expanded their options for producing products and chemicals for markets other than transportation fuels. For example, the Canadian firm Lignol Energy has refocused away from ethanol toward other chemical products that could be produced from wood wastes. A new company, Anellotech, is developing a catalytic pyrolysis technology that converts wood waste and other agricultural residue for use in the chemicals industry and as fuel additives for gasoline producers. Anellotech indicated that its technology may ultimately be applied to produce transportation fuels such as gasoline and diesel.

Whereas wood pellet and wood-to-electricity projects use proven technologies, we do not yet have a successful, commercial-scale facility that converts wood to liquid fuel. Still, entrepreneurs continue to work on the technical issues and develop markets for the future.

CHAPTER FIVE

Sources of Wood for Energy

The United States benefits from its endowment of forests. Of the 2.1 billion acres of land in the United States, nearly one-third is forested. Forest renewability and the seemingly abundant supplies make wood raw materials attractive to new wood bioenergy projects. However, wood raw materials have existing users—mills that produce lumber, plywood, oriented-strand board (OSB), paper and paperboard, and a variety of composite materials. In addition, wood raw material markets, unlike national agriculture markets, rely on imperfect information because supply, demand, and pricing flow through an opaque system. This makes financiers of wood energy projects uncomfortable, especially those used to long-term contracts for coal or other raw materials.

TYPES OF BIOMASS FEEDSTOCKS

Most woody biomass facilities intend to use the by-products of forestry operations for feedstock. These include mill residue, logging slash, land-clearing debris from residential developments, and debris from city parks and street trees. Most of these resources are deemed "underutilized": they have no primary purpose and are often left in the woods, burned, or hauled to landfills. Some in the forest industry, however, are concerned that emerging biomass facilities will compete with pulp and paper mills, which already use mill residue.

Given the lack of market infrastructure for logging residue or urban tree waste at a large scale, biomass facilities will have to coordinate with loggers and tree services. Loggers, for example, will not invest in additional equipment to process and transport logging residue unless they know they can sell it to a dependable local market. Because of such market development challenges, many in the forest products industry believe that bioenergy plants may turn to wood that is already bought and sold in the marketplace. Woody biomass facilities would then compete with forest industry users for raw materials, likely increasing the prices of wood. In sum, the locations of forest industry operations and mills, and the effects of a woody biomass facility on raw material flows and raw material prices in a given local "wood basket," are linked.

Developers of new projects can be vague about the raw materials that their projects will use. They may be trying to protect their strategy during start-up and avoid alerting potential opponents, or attempting to conceal a lack of procurement agreements or evolving business plans. Early press releases often emphasize use of waste materials, even though engineers and project developers prefer high-quality feedstocks, such as mill residue, clean chips, or roundwood. Here is a breakdown of expected feedstocks by project type:

- *Pellet plants* typically need a clean fuel to produce a consistent and clean-burning end product. Sawdust is preferred, but supplies are limited. Therefore, some projects, like Green Circle Bio Energy, Inc., in Florida, purchase pulpwood-sized roundwood and chip it themselves. Another option for pellet facilities is to purchase "clean" in-woods chips (logging residue free of bark and needle debris).

- *Wood-to-electricity projects* (boilers) can accept a larger range of feedstocks. These include "dirty" chips (logging residue that contains bark and needles), urban waste material, such as wood pallet scraps and shavings, and sometimes pulpwood. The wood must be free of chemical contaminants. Just-opened wood biopower projects prefer clean material to optimize the efficiency of the facility before loosening the raw material specifications, which would reduce delivered raw material costs.

- *Liquid fuel projects* could use the same range of feedstock as wood-to-electricity: logging waste, mill waste, chips, and urban waste. Most likely, however, they will require a less variable feedstock for their processes. For example, one announced cellulosic ethanol plant expects to purchase clean chips during its initial two years of operation. As its process improves, it might expand the range of feedstock to include logging residue and dirty chips. However, as of yet, there is no commercial-scale biofuel project operating in the United States to give a real example.

A mobile loader places roundwood on a log truck. Roundwood pulpwood is an established product in forest markets, and most loggers have equipment designed to handle it efficiently.

Another way to think about the supplies and sources of wood biomass for energy is to consider the connection between these sources and forests themselves (Figure 5.1). Primary sources are derived from forests directly, secondary sources are residue from forest products manufacturing processes, and tertiary supplies come from indirect, downstream sources unrelated to forest management or forest products mills, such as material recycled from landfills or recovered from demolition.

Most secondary sources of woody biomass are in limited supply. Pulp mills consume all of their own pulping liquors, for example, because it is already paid for and on-site. Sawmills use much of their own residue as boiler fuel or have dedicated, nearby markets for high-quality chips. To become a source for biomass energy, this residue would have to be diverted from current users and uses.

Current competition for pulpwood and in-woods chips varies locally, depending on the landowner and wood supply agreements already in place. The primary users of pulpwood nationwide are pulp mills, followed by OSB manufacturers, and then, in the Lake States and Midwest, bioenergy facilities. The supply chain and infrastructure exist to capture primary wood

Wood Biomass Supplies Categorized by Source

SUPPLY CATEGORY	SOURCES
Primary	Roundwood pulpwood and in-woods chips harvested in forests
	Logging residue from harvest operations
	Trees from land-clearing activities
	Fuel reduction thinnings in overgrown forests
Secondary	Manufacturing residues from sawmills and other forest product facilities
	Pulping (i.e., black) liquor
Tertiary	Cleaned, woody municipal solid waste, such as yard clippings, trash
	Clean construction and demolition debris

Figure 5.1. Woody biomass can be primary (sourced directly from the woods), secondary (a product of manufacturing), or tertiary (postconsumer waste material).

biomass in the form of pulpwood roundwood for wood-using facilities. The supply chain for clean in-woods chips for pulp production exists in areas near pulp mills that purchase clean chips, although roundwood production is by far the norm at a large scale. If demand for pulpwood and in-woods chips increases substantially, the logging industry would grow, with more logging contractors, more employees per logging contractor, more equipment to produce greater volumes of pulpwood, more chippers and grinders to process the material, and more chip vans to transport the material from the woods to the biomass facility.

Harvest operations generate significant volumes of forest residue, a by-product that is consistently cited as a source of underutilized biomass. Even though pulpmills today accept top wood and other small pieces that would once have been left in the forest, residue from timber harvesting could provide additional biomass volume.

Another potential source is dedicated energy crops grown on plantations. Short-rotation woody crops of poplar or willow grown specifically for conversion into energy products could provide substantial volumes of woody biomass. Unlike corn for ethanol, these crops do not compete with food or animal feed. Dedicated energy crops could be grown on idle acreage within short hauling distances of wood-using bioenergy plants. However,

Logging residue and wood from land clearing can prove difficult and expensive to handle if it is contaminated with soil and sand.

these crops require intensive management and fertilizer, and as of 2011, the economics of these efforts have yet to justify the investment.

BIOMASS SUPPLY AVAILABILITY

The U.S. Forest Service manages a continuous forest census that characterizes America's forests, called the Forest Inventory and Analysis (FIA) program. FIA maintains a comprehensive database, which can be downloaded directly from its website, and summarizes forest supply information in its regularly published *Forest Resources of the United States*.

The net area of forestland in the United States stabilized in the early 20th century and has constituted a third of total land area since the 1920s. Approximately 70 percent of the original forested area of the "New World" remains in forest cover, though the structure, composition, and distribution of these forests differ substantially from when European settlers first arrived.

Since 1932, forest area in the United States has increased by about 1 percent because improvements in agricultural productivity, mainly mechanization, have released cropland to return to forest. An estimated 20 million acres of grain fields and pastures were no longer needed when gasoline tractors replaced horses and mules. Since the 1950s, technological advancements in growing trees—such as genetics, site preparation, weed control, and

ENVIRONMENTAL EFFECTS OF REMOVING WOODY BIOMASS

Could the removal of woody debris from forested sites deplete forest soils and reduce the productivity of these sites to grow trees? Research on the environmental consequences of biomass harvesting suggests that in general, removing logging residue has minimal long-term effects on site productivity, especially if sites are fertilized. Most sites are expected to recover within five years of harvesting (Hacker 2005; Westbrook et al. 2007; Eisenbies et al. 2009). Effects will be greater on sites that already have nutrient deficiencies or poor soils. Poor-quality sites may require more fertilization or more woody material to be left on site.

As woody debris decays in the forest, it releases minerals and nutrients back into the soil; removing the debris thus removes a source of soil nutrients. To mitigate this effect, some U.S. states have biomass harvesting guidelines that seek to keep sufficient woody material on site to replenish forest soils and maintain structure on the forest floor to prevent erosion. Loggers in all states are encouraged or required to follow best management practices (BMPs) when conducting a timber harvest, including in states without biomass harvesting guidelines. Although BMPs are not specific to biomass harvesting, they help protect site quality by preventing erosion and maintaining water quality.

Timber harvesting produces volumes of logging residue and slash that could be used for bioenergy, but much of that material is difficult or uneconomic to collect. Timber-harvesting operations do not collect all the logging slash produced, especially if it is not located centrally on the harvest site. Going back over a harvest site to collect residue is costly and inefficient. The price of any feedstock must offset or exceed the cost of collecting it; biomass material, with the lowest value of all timber products produced in a harvest operation, may not justify the cost and effort. In addition, woody biomass material that contains dirt or sand is undesirable for bioenergy applications because the foreign material interferes with combustion.

fertilization—have helped tree growth outpace tree removals. As of 2006, U.S. forest growth exceeded removals by more than 58 percent, and forest growth totaled 26 billion cubic feet of wood per year.

Environmental groups and forests products firms are concerned about the potential effects of increased woody biomass use on the sustainability of U.S. forest supplies. Researchers have attempted to quantify the volume of biomass supplies that are available for biomass energy. In 2005, the

"Billion Ton Study," published by the Department of Energy (DOE) and United States Department of Agriculture (USDA) with contributions from the U.S. Forest Service, assessed the feasibility of producing sufficient biomass to displace 30 percent of current U.S. petroleum consumption. This would require about 1.3 billion dry tons of biomass feedstock annually, of which 368 million dry tons (28 percent) would come from forestland and wood-based sources (Figure 5.2). The research had some limitations, however, including unrealistic estimates of how much woody biomass was accessible and cost-effective to recover.

DOE revisited the 2005 research to account for cost constraints on availability and published an update to the "Billion Ton Study" in August 2011. This update found that a total of 473 million dry tons of biomass would be available in 2012 at $60 per dry ton or less. By 2030, the total available biomass would increase to 1.1 billion tons at $60 per dry ton or less. Forest biomass available for new users at $60 per dry ton or less was estimated at 97 million dry tons in 2012, and 102 million dry tons in 2030.

In 2010, the American Forest & Paper Association commissioned Forisk Consulting to assess which of the volumes estimated in the "Billion Ton Study" would be readily available—that is, both currently unused by other wood raw material consumers and economically affordable under feasible harvesting operations. For example, logging residue that could be collected by adding a small chipper to a traditional logging operation was considered readily available, whereas logging residue that required a significant capital investment or interfered with normal logging production was deemed unavailable.

The research found that at least 50 million dry tons of woody biomass may be available in the United States for evolving wood bioenergy markets. The total demand for possible wood bioenergy projects approximates 60 million dry tons by 2021, but wood demand from projects likely to succeed approaches 35 million dry tons. On a national level, enough woody biomass is available from forest, urban, and mill residue to satisfy the need for wood for energy. At a cost of about $60 per dry ton, 2 million to 5 million dry tons of conventional pulpwood will be available, but this is not enough to supply all announced projects. Large-scale demand for pulpwood or clean chips will drive costs beyond $60 per dry ton. The national assessments do not evaluate the sustainability of wood raw material supplies for

Estimated U.S. Forest Biomass Supplies

	BILLION TON 2005	BILLION TON 2011 UPDATE*		FORISK 2010
	SUPPLY	TOTAL	POTENTIAL (UNUSED)	READILY AVAILABLE
	Million dry tons per year			
Fuelwood	52	38	0	0
Manufacturing residue	145	39	7	2
Urban wood residue	47	46	32	8
Logging residue**	64	40	40	28
Fuel treatments to reduce fire hazards***	60	3	3	0
Unused pulpwood-sized materials		2	2	5
Other removal residue		12	12	11
Total	368	180	97	54

Figure 5.2. Recent reports estimate that of the 180 million dry tons generated per year, 97 million dry tons per year are unused and only 54 million dry tons are readily available. Note that the Forisk 2010 study excluded fuel treatment harvests, which may be an additional source of biomass.

*For the year 2012 at $60 per dry ton. Totals may not sum due to rounding.
** The "Billion Ton 2011 Update" combines fuel treatment volumes with logging residue.
*** Treatment thinnings on other forestland are reported separately in the "Billion Ton 2011 Update." We report the treatment thinnings on other forestland under "Fuel treatments to reduce fire hazards."

a given wood bioenergy project in a given location. To be truly useful, wood market analysis must be local and assess uniquely local wood supplies, wood demand, raw material prices, and wood bioenergy projects.

The 50 million dry tons of readily available raw material translates to almost 100 million green tons. Total wood use by the forest products industry in 2005 was an estimated 522 million green tons but would fall to 516 million green tons in 2015 and then rise to 534 million tons by 2020. Of the 100 million green tons available for new users, logging residue represents the single largest source (57 percent), and mill residue represents the smallest source (3 percent).

A closer look at logging residuals alone indicates the potential for increasing supplies as demand grows. If demand for logging residue increases, prices for the raw material could rise and create the market incentive to get currently unused logging residue to wood bioenergy facilities. Figure 5.3

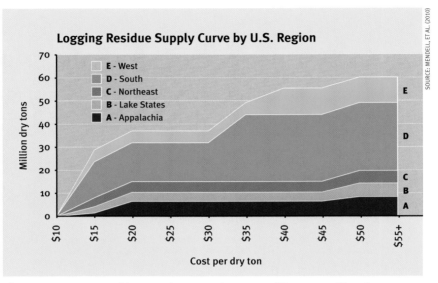

Figure 5.3. At a cost of $15 per dry ton or less, 28 million tons of logging residue is available. This volume represents roundwood-to-logging residue ratios of 3:1 to 6:1. An additional 8.2 million dry tons could come from logging operations with roundwood-to-residue ratios below 3:1 but would require more loading time and possibly larger chippers.

summarizes a supply curve for capturing residuals. Increased use of forest residuals could support efforts to mitigate fire risk by removing excess wood fuels from overloaded forests.

Bioenergy supply opportunities will develop when existing harvest operations expand to bring in more wood or wood residue for energy. These efforts will largely piggyback on the existing forest industry supply chain, relying on existing logging operations. In this sense, wood bioenergy simply represents another forest product. Stand-alone operations dedicated to harvesting or growing wood for energy will remain rare until the markets grow and economics improve.

CHAPTER SIX

Wood Bioenergy Markets and Public Policy

The management and use of wood affects people and organizations with interests ranging from manufacturing and private property rights to conservation and the environment. Forests serve a broad range of human needs that require, at some level, prioritizing. However, in practice, each forest cannot satisfy every need. Public policy provides one mechanism for designating priorities, managing activities, and allocating resources in ways that affect how and when forests and wood raw materials can be used. This is especially true for evolving wood bioenergy markets because bioenergy investment and production are largely driven by public policy.

Public policy debates related to wood bioenergy center first on whether supply and demand decisions should be made primarily by the government (through incentives, subsidies, and mandates) or by the marketplace. Free-market economists would argue that resource decisions are best made by private owners because governments are coercive but markets are voluntary. Yet, when public interests (e.g., green energy goals and energy independence) are involved, government involvement can advance values that may not be incorporated into market transactions.

Historically, wood bioenergy was influenced by policy, first through legislation regulating electric utilities, and second through efforts to increase renewable energy generation in the United States. More recent policy efforts can be organized into three general areas: renewable energy targets, emissions permitting, and wood biomass production.

RENEWABLE ENERGY TARGETS

Specific policy efforts encouraging or mandating additional wood biopower include federal and state bills that would establish renewable portfolio standards (RPS) or renewable electricity standards (RES) or renewable fuel standards (RFS). Specific examples of legislation to expand renewable energy in the United States include the Energy Independence and Security Act (EISA) of 2007 and various farm bills.

Potential legislative mandates on electricity generation are implemented through state RPS and federal RES programs. These include targets for renewable electricity sources that give utilities an incentive to support wood-to-electricity plants and wood cogeneration projects. For example, in 2009 and 2010, Congress proposed three national RES levels to require certain electricity suppliers to provide at least 15 to 20 percent of the electricity they sell from renewable energy sources by 2020–2021. Eligible renewable sources include wind, solar, geothermal, renewable biomass, biogas and biofuels derived exclusively from renewable biomass, qualified hydropower commissioned after 1992, and marine and hydrokinetic sources. Although none of these bills passed, it is likely that new proposals will be made.

Loan guarantees and grants targeted at encouraging renewable energy supplies have also been proposed as a way to help meet renewable energy targets. These include programs described in the sidebar in Chapter 4 associated with DOE's Office of Energy and Renewable Energy and Energy Loan Programs Office, USDA's Rural Utilities Service, and other activities funded at the state level.

For liquid transportation fuels, the U.S. government began mandating the use of fuel ethanol and renewable biofuels with the Energy Security Act of 1980. However, recent acts channel efforts through renewable fuel standards. The RFS program, created under the Energy Policy Act of 2005, established the first renewable fuel volume mandate in the United States. Under this program, the EPA implements regulations to ensure that transportation fuels contain minimum volumes of renewable fuel. The Energy Independence and Security Act of 2007 expanded the RFS program to increase the volume of renewable fuel required to be blended into transportation fuel from 9 billion gallons in 2008 to 36 billion by 2022. This increase in renewable fuel requirements—referred to as RFS2—caused excitement regarding cellulosic biofuel because it would increase the demand

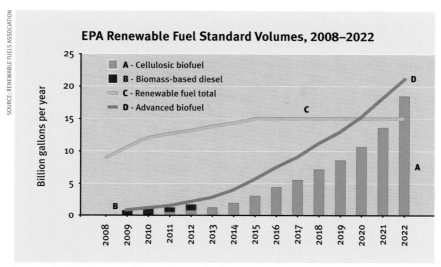

Figure 6.1. The Renewable Fuel Standard requires fuel producers to sell specified volumes of conventional biofuel, advanced biofuel, and cellulosic biofuel in the United States. Conventional biofuel is ethanol made from corn starch. Advanced biofuel is made from renewable materials other than cornstarch and can include cellulosic biofuels and biomass-based diesel. Cellulosic biofuel is made from cellulose, hemicellulose, or lignin from renewable biomass.

for cellulosic biofuel. Companies formed to commercialize cellulosic biofuels, including ethanol, some of which would be made from woody biomass.

Under RFS2, the EPA adjusts the volume standard each year based on the actual capacity of operational biofuel plants. For 2011, the EPA reduced the volume requirement for cellulosic biofuel because of low production estimates. Still, the EPA maintained the advanced biofuels standard at 1.35 billion gallons (Figure 6.1). The percentage standards represent the percentage of all motor fuel that must be renewable. Altogether, approximately 8 percent of all fuel is required to come from renewable sources.

So far, the only large-scale renewable motor fuel in the United States has been corn ethanol. However, the EPA caps corn ethanol's contribution to the total 2022 RFS goal at 15 billion gallons (about 42 percent of the 36 billion gallon total), and there is a technical barrier associated with gasoline-ethanol blending limits. With a 10 percent ethanol blend, the maximum amount of ethanol that could be sold is 13 billion gallons (10 percent of the 130 billion gallons of fuel sold in the United States), which approximates annual usage as of 2010. This limit on the total amount of ethanol in the U.S. market could discourage investment in cellulosic ethanol projects. Drop-in fuels (see Chapter 4) are a direct substitute for gasoline and are not subject to the blending wall.

EMISSIONS PERMITTING

Another policy that encourages the use of wood for energy involves regulations on the emissions of greenhouse gases (GHGs) from energy plants powered by fossil fuels. The regulatory efforts began with the Clean Air Act of 1970 and are implemented by the EPA, which was established in 1971. One recent effort derived from the Clean Air Act is the Greenhouse Gas Tailoring Rule.

The Tailoring Rule covers facilities that exceed certain thresholds for emissions of carbon dioxide and five other greenhouse gases. The EPA expects that approximately 900 new projects and facility modifications per year will require permitting for GHG emissions. The final Tailoring Rule announced in 2010 did not distinguish between biomass electricity and fossil fuel electricity; all power plant emissions were to be regulated in the same manner, regardless of the fuel type. This caused much concern in the biomass industry, which had previously been considered carbon neutral (see sidebar on page 50). Many biomass projects were put on hold because of possible increased permitting costs and fears that biomass energy would not be considered renewable.

Concerns about GHG permitting for wood biomass projects centered on the treatment of carbon emissions. Typically, carbon dioxide emissions from biomass combustion do not count toward regulatory thresholds because they do not increase net global concentrations of carbon dioxide: the burning of plant biomass materials emits carbon dioxide, which contains the same carbon that was sequestered by the plant when it was growing. It is argued, then, that the combustion of biofuels does not result in net carbon dioxide emissions; it is part of a natural carbon cycle commonly considered carbon neutral.

In 2011, the EPA announced that GHG permitting requirements for facilities using biomass to make electricity would be deferred for three years, while it gathers more information on biomass-related carbon dioxide emissions. Until the EPA makes a final decision, biomass facilities are not subject to GHG permitting regulations, but the Tailoring Rule may have stalled interest and progress in wood-consuming biopower projects in the United States.

Stand-alone wood-to-electricity projects, biomass cofiring at coal burning power plants, and wood-burning cogeneration plants at forest industry mills stand to gain or lose depending on how carbon dioxide emissions are handled. About 87 percent of the operating and announced wood bioenergy projects and 92 percent of cogeneration plants at forest products mills in the continental United States will be affected by the decision on greenhouse gas permitting.

WOOD BIOMASS PRODUCTION

Legislative efforts to increase the supply and availability of woody biomass for energy uses include the Biomass Crop Assistance Program (BCAP), authorized as part of the Food, Conservation, and Energy Act of 2008. The rationale for BCAP was that accessing forest residuals was costly, and this cost was constraining bioenergy projects.

The purpose of the program is to "assist agricultural and forest land owners and operators with the establishment and production of eligible crops including wood biomass...for conversion to bioenergy, and the collection, harvest, storage, and transportation of eligible materials for use in a biomass conversion facility."

BCAP faced three practical challenges. First, large portions of qualifying materials—such as in-woods chips, residual chips, and bark—have existing markets. The intent of BCAP was to establish supplies for woody biomass facilities, not to divert raw materials from existing users to biomass energy users. Second, wood markets interrelate; they are not stand-alone supply chains unaffected by other forest harvesting activities. Logging residuals are by-products of standard logging operations; they are not produced independently. Third, subsidies could cause imbalances in the marketplace by encouraging wood suppliers to sell their raw material for fuelwood or residuals to qualify for the crop assistance program, harming traditional wood processors like pulp and composite mills and creating winners and losers.

The program was revised in 2010 to address the issues with feedstock markets and to address sustainability concerns. The new ruling requires

CARBON NEUTRALITY OF FOREST BIOENERGY

Renewable differs from *carbon neutral*, but the two terms are closely related, and both are associated with "green" energy. Biomass is considered renewable because it can be replenished and regenerated naturally in relatively short time periods. In contrast, fossil fuels, such as coal, oil, and natural gas, take millions of years to form and are not considered renewable.

The carbon neutrality of wood used for energy has to do with trees' natural role in the biogenic carbon cycle—removing carbon from the atmosphere through photosynthesis, storing it, and emitting it into the atmosphere through respiration and decay (Figure 6.2). When a power plant burns biomass to make electricity, it releases the stored carbon into the atmosphere. Because the same amounts of carbon are sequestered and released, forest bioenergy is said to be carbon neutral.

A *Science* article (Searchinger et al. 2009) argued that bioenergy was not inherently carbon neutral and proposed that policymakers regulate carbon emissions at the source (i.e., power plant or tailpipe), whether the feedstock is fossil fuel or biomass. One argument supporting this approach is that trees may be better carbon sinks, or storage units, if left to grow.

Whether forest bioenergy is carbon neutral depends largely on which carbon accounting method is used. There are two basic ways to measure a system's carbon flows (capture, storage, and release to the atmosphere): the carbon stocks approach and the carbon debt approach. The forest industry advocates the carbon

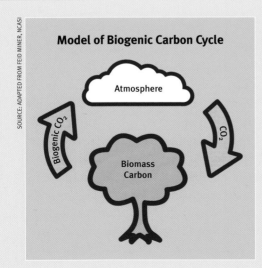

Figure 6.2. Using forest biomass to produce electricity is said to be carbon neutral because the process releases biogenic carbon— the same carbon that the trees would release to the atmosphere through natural processes. The argument against the carbon neutrality of forest biomass rests on the time lag between carbon release (burning) and carbon capture for a single stand of trees. Advocates of forest biomass argue that carbon flows should be measured on a landscape level and consider multiple stands of trees.

stocks method because it provides a landscape-level view that considers several forest stands (groups of trees that constitute management units) in a landscape. Carbon losses from harvesting one stand are offset by the carbon uptake of growing trees in neighboring stands. In contrast, the carbon debt approach focuses on a single stand. Carbon that is released through burning biomass must be regained through the regrowth of that particular stand in the future. With the carbon debt approach, bioenergy is not inherently carbon neutral because at the time the biomass is removed, the system has a carbon debt.

Researchers at the Manomet Center for Conservation Sciences (Walker 2010) applied a type of carbon debt approach to analyze greenhouse gas emissions in Massachusetts. The Manomet study compared biomass energy emissions directly with fossil fuel emissions, with the important assumption that biomass emits more carbon dioxide per unit of energy than fossil fuels. The timing and magnitude of the carbon debt and dividends depend highly on the technology types chosen to replace fossil fuels and on landowner management activities.

After reviewing research on carbon accounting and the carbon neutrality of biomass energy, the EPA will determine how to regulate GHG emissions from biomass plants. If bioenergy is not deemed carbon neutral, then its renewability may come into question. And if biomass is no longer considered renewable and cannot be used to meet renewable portfolio standards, then few incentives exist for producers to generate power from biomass.

biomass conversion facilities to prove that eligible BCAP materials are by-products of preventive treatments; eligible materials cannot have an existing or higher-value market. In fact, sawdust and mill residuals are excluded. The revised program also requires that producers follow a conservation plan. Still, concerns about eligibility and funding hinder the development of biomass energy. As of April 2011, only three facilities had enrolled in BCAP—two in South Dakota and one in Iowa.

Like the Tailoring Rule, BCAP directly affects private investment decisions, and private investment decisions will affect the capacity of the United States to produce energy from wood. For wood-to-electricity projects, primary concerns are financing and legislative or regulatory certainty. The practical challenges of managing forests and building wood-using facilities depend on confidence in long-term stability and demand. The role played by public policy can effectively align interests or deter investment in evolving wood bioenergy markets.

CHAPTER SEVEN

Looking Forward

The history of U.S. forests is a story of natural resilience, economic markets, and political priorities. The natural regrowth of U.S. forests since 1920 and the active management initiated by major forest owners has allowed long-term increases in forest productivity. Timber volume per acre in the United States has increased nearly 50 percent since 1952, and U.S. forest growth has exceeded harvest since the 1940s.

Wood has a long history as a fuel source for energy in the United States. This has been driven by both convenience and necessity, as when the first settlers and later the steamship and railroad builders had ready access to abundant wood supplies and limited access to other fuels, such as coal. Today wood bioenergy faces several practical challenges.

What is wood worth? For the forest products industry, the value of wood raw materials is largely determined by the value of the end products (i.e., lumber and pulp) and by the local wood basket surrounding their operating facilities. Determining the value of wood is critical because it determines the appropriate forest management strategies, logging equipment, and manufacturing technologies. Timberland owners make forest management decisions today based on the expected buyers of their wood 15 or 25 years or more into the future. From their perspective, wood bioenergy is simply another forest product.

Demand for biomass for energy has implications for the timing, processing, and transportation of wood raw materials. A payment scheme based on weight, for example, encourages the seller to sell heavier trees. Because trees are 50 percent moisture, payment on a green ton basis benefits the seller.

A payment scheme based on energy content would encourage the seller to sell wood on a dry ton basis, since the water in the wood reduces its energy value. That, in turn, could change the way wood is processed and hauled. Today in the Southeast, the same logging crew harvests the timber, processes it, and transports it in quick succession; with this "hot" logging, the wood has no time to dry. If the wood is to be sold in dry tons, harvesters would switch to "cold" logging, in which the harvested wood is left stacked at roadside for several months before being processed and hauled to market.

There are also implications for how log haulers are compensated. Haulers typically charge per ton-mile, based on weight and distance. In the future their charges might be based on energy content instead of weight. Loggers, haulers, and landowners will need to be able to measure the energy content of wood.

How much wood is worth may ultimately depend on any public policy incentives that encourage biomass energy relative to traditional wood markets. Investments made primarily in response to government mandates and subsidies for biomass are riskier than those made on the inherent value of wood for energy absent those incentives. Policies and subsidies can change, regardless of the private market interests. The EPA's deferred decision about regulating emissions from wood-using facilities is one example.

Where should chipping (processing) occur? At first, wood bioenergy plants sought to minimize the capital expenditures associated with wood yards and chipping facilities by using in-woods chips and materials that were already processed. On-site chipping, however, increases raw material flexibility, security of supply, and quality. Where wood is processed determines what equipment is needed, who buys it, and how much capital investment is required.

How secure and efficient is the procurement system? The supply chain for woody biomass is evolving, raising questions about security and efficiency for the forest products procurement system. Moving more wood, and many types of wood products, to new markets increases the risk of theft. Loggers and wood suppliers will likely need more vehicles and greater flexibility in scheduling. To achieve sustainable forest management certification, suppliers and buyers will need to document and track wood at each point in the chain, from forest to facility.

A small in-woods chipper blows fresh fuel chips into a chip van for transport to a pulp mill furnace. The capacity of loggers to produce fuel chips is market specific and varies widely throughout the United States. Overall, biomass markets are small and still developing relative to the mature, high-volume wood markets for traditional forest products, such as lumber and paper.

Wood biomass or fiber supply agreements are one way to mitigate the risks associated with biomass procurement and supplies and to reassure bioenergy project managers and investors. The forest industry uses wood supply agreements, often with terms of 10 years or more, to ensure volumes and negotiate pricing. Traditional wood supply agreements have cemented existing forest-to-mill relationships, where buyers and sellers have long known each other. In the bioenergy market, however, participants continue their courtship: supply agreements would help independent bioenergy developers; timberland owners approach long-term commitments to new projects and technologies with caution.

WOOD BIOENERGY AND FOREST INDUSTRY

Wood bioenergy markets and forest owners must operate in competitive markets with real people, rational incentives, and political implications. Forest economists have long studied forest owners' responses to market changes to see how their investment and harvesting decisions change as

prices and other incentives shift. Generally, timber markets and forest owners adjust to changes in prices, supplies, rotation ages, and harvest levels to
find a supply-and-demand equilibrium. Forestland owners make rational
decisions and do not seek to satisfy policy targets (e.g., for renewable energy
production) unless the economics make sense. Policy decisions that provide
economic incentives create frameworks for changing landowner decisions.

Wood suppliers and loggers adapt to new markets incrementally.
According to a study by RE Consulting and INR LLC in Massachusetts,
there are 101 approaches to harvesting forest biomass, only some of which
are common in each region of the country. Loggers apply systems that inte-
grate smoothly and inexpensively with existing forest operations. The
forestry profession consists of local entrepreneurs with a long tradition of
adapting to shifting markets.

There are concerns that emerging bioenergy demand will "vacuum" U.S.
forests, leaving nothing behind but stumps and needles. Similar worries
emerged with growing fuelwood use in the early 1800s, with the Industrial
Revolution in the late 1800s, and when pulp mills expanded in size and
scope during the 20th century. The feared timber famines never occurred.
Instead, U.S. pulp mills' consumption rose from 8 million tons of pulpwood for paper and paperboard in 1910 to 135 million tons in 1965 and
peaked at 265 million tons in 1994. Many factors helped the country avert
timber shortages, but of primary importance were government and industry investments to protect the forest from wildfire, scientific information
on which to base forest management decisions, and tax rules that allowed
industry to make long-term investments. Throughout the century, forest
owners and wood suppliers adapted through improved forest management,
incremental growth of logging operations, and use of previously unused
wood raw materials—all alongside an increasing focus on safety, certification, and environmental management. For example, best management
practices (BMPs) have helped maintain and protect water quality.

In forestry, where landownership and management plans span decades,
we benefit by understanding the markets and technologies as they actually
function today. The process for locating, financing, constructing, and operating bioenergy projects is complicated and difficult, and those involved in
the wood-using industries change incrementally, adapting to new markets.

SUCCESSFUL WOOD BIOENERGY PROJECTS

Economic development professionals, investors, and organizations consider-
ing a wood bioenergy project in their communities or in their portfolios can
look for the signs of a successful biomass project—the same characteristics
that would make it eligible for financing.

Viable technology. The technology to convert wood biomass to energy must
be proven at commercial scale and be capable of generating a reliable quantity
and quality of product at realistic rates of efficiency. For a project with
unproven technologies, financiers and investors must have a realistic prob-
ability for success, and public representatives must appreciate its speculative
nature—high risk, high reward.

Committed customers. The project must have customers committed to purchasing the energy outputs for a specific price and period. If it will connect to
the electricity grid, transmission must be secured and available. If it will export
pellets, access to ports and shipping must be confirmed. The agreements and
terms associated with these commitments represent obligations that affect the
creditworthiness and attractiveness of the project to the lenders and investors
who will assess the risks and viability of the project.

Reliable and sustainable feedstock. Wood biomass feedstocks identified for
the facility must be both accessible and sustainable. These two characteristics
differ. Accessibility means that landowners are willing to sell material that can
be feasibly harvested, collected, and transported. Sustainability means that
the expected market demand for this material cannot deplete the supplies
over time. Projects that use multiple feedstock types and sources can mitigate
supply risk and help protect against changes in wood markets over time.

Project site and permits. The site of the proposed plant should be purchased
or optioned and have access to utilities, nearby transportation (rail, roads, or
ports), water supplies, and space for expansion or wood yards or storage.
Project location is critical because transportation of the raw material is the
highest variable cost: it should be close to the raw material sources and far
from feedstock competitors. Lastly, local attitudes toward the project are
important. Will the local community welcome the jobs or oppose the project?

Economic viability. Ultimately, the project must be profitable under whatever
criteria are applied by the investor or development agency. The cost estimates
should be realistic, with measurable benchmarks to evaluate construction and
operation. Ideally, the financial analysis will indicate a profit even without tax
credits or government subsidies so that the project can stand on its own,
regardless of any policy changes.

Several factors could deter the expanded use of wood for energy. First, wood biomass firms could struggle, or lack the incentive, to solve the industry's operational difficulties in a cost-effective manner. Second, technological challenges for converting wood to energy, especially for liquid fuels, could prove especially stubborn. Third, policy decisions could undermine the market. One example would be a policy that subsidizes alternative energy types, such as nuclear, at higher rates than for wood. These challenges are both practical and political. However, the broader picture remains encouraging. Next to hydropower, wood is the most important renewable energy source and provides more energy than hydropower during periods of drought or low snow cover in the West.

Forest industry manufacturers are well positioned to increase their production of wood bioenergy, by either increasing boiler capacity or becoming integrated forest biorefineries. Pulp and paper mills currently operate simple biorefineries, recapturing residuals and black liquor to generate power while also producing paper. Advanced operations could include the production of biofuels or industrial chemicals to better use existing forest resources. In addition, locating new biorefineries next to existing pulp mills could generate growth in the industry. Forest products manufacturers are also an experienced source of energy supply. They create their own fuel through procurement and manufacturing processes. They have handled the permitting issues associated with air and water. And they have the ability to manage other logistic issues, such as trucking and processing.

Currently, the wood raw material procurement system is designed to deliver primarily roundwood and mill residue to forest products facilities. The collection and delivery of logging residue and, to a certain degree, in-woods chips are local and not common in all geographic markets. Bioenergy facilities depend on logging residue, mill residue, and in-woods chips to satisfy their raw material needs. In turn, these sources are generated from log harvesting and lumber production. As a result, if no one harvests the primary roundwood for logs or produces lumber, the supplies of residual raw materials needed by woody biomass facilities may not be available.

Incorporating wood into the energy portfolio for the United States could have multiple benefits: renewability, reduced GHG emissions, reduced fire hazards on public forestlands, and less dependence on foreign sources of petroleum. The potential benefits explain why renewable energy from wood

Pulp and paper mills are well-suited to add or expand wood-based energy production on-site. Many of these forest products facilities already operate cogeneration plants to provide electricity and process steam to run their mills. Howe Sound Pulp and Paper Ltd. in British Columbia is a good example.

has become a priority in other countries and continues to gain support in the United States. Smart use of available wood raw materials can support long-term forest health and energy objectives in the United States.

Wood bioenergy markets will develop as investors, policymakers, and forest owners work through the logistical, political, and technical challenges of growing a new subsector within an existing industry. As in the past, forest owners will assess their options in bioenergy markets with a view to the long term, and wood suppliers and loggers will adapt to new markets incrementally. New wood markets do not create a frenzy of forest harvesting. Rather, the public can expect improved forest management, incremental growth of logging operations, and utilization of previously underused wood raw materials. In the end, wood bioenergy is another forest product.

We would like to thank the many individuals and firms that made this publication possible. Thank you to Steve Anderson and the Forest History Society for approaching us to write this book and for his thoughtful edits. We also thank Sally Atwater for her thorough edits and detailed suggestions to improve the accessibility of this book. Wood bioenergy research has been central to our work for several years, and we enjoyed and appreciated the opportunity to summarize years of work into an accessible format for a broader audience.

We sincerely thank the financial sponsors of this effort. These include the Plum Creek Foundation, Forest Investment Associates, National Alliance of Forest Owners, Potlatch Corporation, Price Biostock, The Westervelt Company, U.S. Forest Service Research, and the Lynn W. Day Endowment for Forest History Publications. Without their support, this book would not have been possible.

Thank you to other researchers who provided critical feedback and practical suggestions for improving the manuscript. These include Roger Sedjo and Douglas MacCleery.

We thank our fellow colleagues, Heather Clark at Forisk and Tim Sydor at the Center for Forest Business at the University of Georgia, who assisted in the original wood bioenergy research and supported the improvement of this book.

Annual removal net volume of growing-stock trees removed from the inventory during a specific year through harvesting, forest management activities, or land clearing.

Ash the noncombustible component of fuel.

Best management practice (BMP) a practice that is determined by a state or planning agency to be the most effective and practicable means of controlling point and nonpoint source pollutants.

Biomass plant-derived organic material that is renewable, including wood waste, dedicated energy crops and trees, agricultural crops or waste, and municipal or mill waste.

British thermal unit (Btu) a standard unit of energy equal to the heat required to raise the temperature of 1 pound (0.45 kg) of water 1°F (0.56°C).

Carbon sequestration the process of removing carbon from the atmosphere and storing it.

Carbon accounting the measurement of carbon flows (capture, storage, and release to the atmosphere) of a system.

Carbon sink anything that stores carbon; a carbon reservoir.

Cellulosic ethanol ethyl alcohol produced from cellulose, the structural component of the cell walls of plants.

Clean chips wood chips made from logs that have been debarked and are free of needles and leaves; clean chips are high-quality and can be used to make pulp or paper.

Cofiring mixing two fuels for combustion in the same chamber.

Cogeneration the production of electricity and another form of energy jointly; combined heat and power (CHP).

Cord a stack of fuelwood that measures 4 by 4 by 8 feet (128 cubic feet).

Construction and demolition (C&D) debris waste materials left over from building homes or other structures or from tearing down buildings.

Dirty chips wood chips made from whole trees or logging residue that contains bark, needles, and leaves; dirty chips are often used for energy purposes.

Drop-in fuel a fuel that is interchangeable and compatible with conventional fuel. A drop-in fuel does not require adaptation of the engine, fuel system, or fuel distribution network and can be used in currently available engines in pure form and/or blended in any amount with conventional fuel, other substitute fuels, or blends.

Ethanol ethyl alcohol, a colorless, flammable liquid produced by the fermentation of sugar and used as a fuel oxygenate.

Forestland land at least 10 percent stocked by forest trees of any size, including land that previously had such tree cover and that will be naturally or artificially regenerated. The minimum area for forestland classification is 1 acre. Tree-covered areas in agricultural production settings, such as fruit orchards, or tree-covered areas in urban settings, such as city parks, are not considered forestland.

Fuelwood wood used for conversion to a form of energy.

Growing stock timber inventory growing on forestland.

Hardwood broad-leaved, deciduous trees.

Kilowatt (kW) a standard unit for expressing the rate of electrical power and useful heat output.

Logging residue unused portions of growing-stock trees cut or killed by tree-harvesting activities (logging) and left in the woods.

Megawatt (MW) a unit of power equal to one million watts, esp. as a measure of the output of a power station.

Municipal solid waste (MSW) trash or garbage that contains a wide variety of items including packaging, food items, newspapers, clothing. Municipal solid waste can contain woody materials such as wood packaging (pallets) and yard trimmings.

Oriented-strand board (OSB) a type of engineered structural panel made from low-value wood raw material; strands, or long chips, of wood are glued together in a specific orientation to form panels. OSB is used in construction and directly competes with plywood.

Pulpwood roundwood, whole-tree chips, or wood residue used for the production of wood pulp.

Renewable portfolio standard (RPS) a state requirement that a certain percentage of electricity generated in the state come from renewable sources.

Residue bark and woody materials generated in primary wood-using mills when roundwood is processed. Examples include edgings, sawdust, shavings, and pulp screenings. Also includes bark and wood residue (both coarse and fine materials), but excludes logging residue.

Roundwood a length of cut tree, also called a log, generally having a round cross section, produced from harvesting trees for industrial or consumer applications.

Softwood coniferous trees, usually evergreen, with needles or scalelike leaves.

Timberland forestland that produces or is capable of producing industrial roundwood and not withdrawn from timber production by law or administrative regulation. The minimum level of productivity is often set at 20+ cubic feet per year in natural stands. Currently inaccessible and inoperable areas are included.

Top the wood of a tree above the merchantable height, including the usable material in the uppermost stem.

Wood pellet a type of fuel burned to produce heat. Pellets are produced from sawdust or dried woody material that is ground into fine particles and compressed into small cylinders, generally 1.5 inches long and ¼ inch in diameter.

Abt, K., J. Fortney, F. Cubbage, and R. Abt. 2010. Going EMO from BCAP. Southern Forest Economics Workers (SOFEW) Presentation, March 16, Pinehurst, North Carolina.

Alig, R. J., A. J. Plantinga, S. E. Ahn, and J. D. Kline. 2003. Land use changes involving forestry in the United States: 1952 to 1997, with projections to 2050. General Technical Report PNW-GTR-587. Portland, Oregon: USDA Forest Service, Pacific Northwest Research Station.

Aust, W. M., and C. R. Blinn. 2004. Forestry best management practices for timber harvesting and site preparation in the eastern United States: An overview of water quality and productivity research during the past 20 years (1982–2002). *Water, Air, & Soil Pollution: Focus* 4: 5–36.

Bergman, R., and J. Zerbe. 2008. Primer on wood biomass for energy. Madison, Wisconsin: USDA Forest Service, Forest Products Laboratory.

Biomass Research and Development. 2010. Glossary. Available at: http://www.usbiomassboard.gov/related_information/glossary.html.

Bullis, K. 2009. Petroleum's long good-bye. *Technology Review* November/December issue. Available at: http://www.technologyreview.com/energy/23670/page1/.

Carroll, G., S. Schoenholtz, B. Young, and E. Dibble. 2004. Effectiveness of forestry streamside management zones in the sand-clay hills of Mississippi: Early indications. *Water, Air, & Soil Pollution: Focus* 4: 275–96.

Connor, P. A. 2010. Energy transitions. The Pardee Papers. No. 12. Boston University. Available at: http://www.bu.edu/pardee/files/2010/11/12-PP-Nov2010.pdf.

Connor, R. C., T. O. Adams, and T. G. Johnson. 2009. Assessing the potential for biomass energy development in South Carolina. Research paper SRS-46. USDA Forest Service, Southern Research Station.

Cubbage, F. W., J. O'Laughlin and C. S. Bullock. 1993. *Forest Resource Policy*. New York: John Wiley & Sons.

Curci, M. J. 2010. Procurement, process, and storage techniques for controlling off-gassing and pellet temperatures. Available at: http://pelletheat.org/wp-content/uploads/2010/08/Off_gassing_study_Curci_2010.pdf.

Database of State Incentives for Renewables and Efficiency. 2011. RPS Policies Map. Available at http://www.dsireusa.org/summarymaps/index.cfm?ee=1&RE=1.

Eisenbies, M. H., Vance, E. D., Aust, W. M., & Seiler, J. R. 2009. Intensive utilization of harvest residues in southern pine plantations: Quantities available and implications for nutrient budgets and sustainable site productivity. *Bioenergy Research* (2): 90–98.

Energy Information Administration. 2000. The federal statutory background of the electric power industry. In *The changing structure of the electric power industry 2000: An update.* Available at http://www.eia.gov/cneaf/electricity/chg_stru_update/chapter4.html.

———. 2009. Annual energy review. Available at http://www.eia.gov/emeu/aer/contents.html

———. 2011. Renewable energy consumption and electricity preliminary statistics 2010. Available at http://www.eia.gov/renewable/annual/preliminary/.

Environmental Protection Agency. 2007. eGRID2007 Version 1.1. Available at http://www.epa.gov/cleanenergy/energy-resources/egrid/index.html.

Forisk Consulting. 2011. Wood bioenergy US database, May. Available at http://www.foriskstore.com/servlet/the-31/Wood-Bioenergy-US/Detail.

Gravelle, J., and T. Link. 2007. Influence of timber harvesting on headwater peak stream temperatures in a northern Idaho watershed. *Forest Science* 53(2): 189–205.

Hacker, J. J. 2005. *Effects of logging residue removal on forest sites: A literature review.* Eau Claire, WI: West Central Wisconsin Regional Planning Commission.

Harris, R. R., K. Sullivan, P. H. Cafferata, J. R. Munn, and K. M. Raucher. 2007. Applications of turbidity monitoring to forest management in California. *Environmental Management* 40: 531–43.

Harris, T., S. Baldwin, and B. Mendell. 2005. Pulpwood and pulp: Long-term history. *Forest Landowner* January/February: 50–51.

Harrison, M. 2006. Pellet fuel potential: The resurgence of wood as a heating source. Ashland, Virginia: Pallet Enterprise. Industrial Reporting, Inc. Available at http://www.palletenterprise.com/articledatabase/view.asp?articleID=1952.

Hearth, Patio, and Barbecue Association. 2011. U.S. hearth statistics. Available at http://www.hpba.org/statistics/hpba-us-hearth-statistics.

Jackson, C. R., D. P. Batzer, S. R. Cross, S. M. Haggerty, and C. A. Sturm. 2007. Headwater streams and timber harvest: Channel, macroinvertebrate, and amphibian response and recovery. *Forest Science* 53(2): 356–70.

Karwan, D. L., J. A. Gravelle, and J. A. Hubbart. 2007. Effects of timber harvest on suspended sediment loads in Mica Creek, Idaho. *Forest Science* 53(2): 181–88.

Lane, J. 2011. EPA approves E15 for model years 2001 and later, for cars, SUVs, and light pickup trucks. *Biofuels Digest.* Available at http://biofuelsdigest.com/bdigest/2011/01/24/ epa-approves-e15-for-model-years-2001-and-later-for-cars-suvs-and-light-pickup-trucks/.

MacCleery, D. W. 1992. *American forests: A history of resilience and recovery.* Durham, North Carolina: Forest History Society.

Mendell, B., and A. H. Lang. 2010a. Screening announced wood bioenergy projects. *FRA Technical Release*, 12(1): 20–21.

———. 2010b. A practical guide for tracking wood-using bioenergy markets. *National Alliance of Forest Owners White Paper* April: 1–10. Available at http://nafoalliance.org/wp-content/uploads/Forisk-A-Practical-Guide-for-Tracking-Wood-Using-Bioenergy.pdf.

Mendell, B., A. H. Lang, and B. Schiamberg. 2011. *Transportation fuels from wood: Investment and market implications of current projects and technologies.* Bogart, Georgia: Forisk Consulting and the Schiamberg Group.

Mendell, B., A. H. Lang, and T. Sydor. 2010. Economic and regional impact analysis of the treatment of biomass energy under the EPA greenhouse gas Tailoring Rule. *National Alliance of Forest Owners White Paper* December: 1–32. Available at http://nafoalliance.org/wp-content/uploads/NAFO-Study-Tailoring-Rule-Economic-Impact-20101214.pdf.

Mendell, B., A. H. Lang, T. Sydor, and S. Freeman. 2010. Availability and sustainability of wood resources for energy generation in the United States. *American Forest & Paper Association White Paper* June: 1–29. Available at: http://www.afandpa.org/temp/Forisk_ Forest_Resource_Study_July_2010.pdf.

Morris, J. F., J. M. Reilly, and S. Paltsev. 2010. Combining a renewable portfolio standard with a cap-and-trade policy: a general equilibrium analysis. Report No. 187. MIT Joint Program on the Science and Policy of Global Change.

Mousdale, D. M. 2010. *Introduction to Biofuels*. Boca Raton, Florida: CRC Press.

Oak Ridge National Laboratory and U.S. Department of Energy. 2010. Biomass energy data book, 3rd edition. Available at http://cta.ornl.gov/bedb/index.shtml.

Perlack, R. D., L. L. Wright, A. F. Turhollow, R. L. Graham, B. J. Stokes, and D. C. Erbach. 2005. Biomass as feedstock for a bioenergy and bioproducts industry: The technical feasibility of a billion-ton annual supply. DOE/GO-102995-2135. ORNL/TM-2005/66.

Perlin, J. 1991. *A Forest Journey*. Cambridge, Massachusetts: Harvard University Press.
———. 2010. Peak wood forges an industrial revolution. *Miller-McCune Magazine*. Available at: http://www.miller-mccune.com/science-environment/peak-wood-forges-an-industrial-revolution-14608/.

Pimentel, D., and T. Patzek. 2005. Ethanol production using corn, switchgrass, and wood; biodiesel production using soybean and sunflower. *Natural Resources Research* 14(1): 65–76.

Pirraglia, A., R. Gonzalez, D. Saloni, and J. Wright. 2010. Wood pellets: An expanding market opportunity. *Biomass Magazine* June. Available at: http://biomassmagazine.com/articles/3858/wood-pellets-an-expanding-market-opportunity.

Rakos, C., and S. Voyles. 2010. Wood use for energy: Experiences and perspectives. Presentation to Forest Products Society "Smallwood" Conference, April 20, Hot Springs, Arkansas.

RE Consulting and Innovative Natural Resource Solutions. 2007. Forest harvesting systems for biomass production: Renewable biomass from the forests of Massachusetts. Massachusetts Division of Energy Resources and Massachusetts Department of Conservation and Recreation. June.

Risbrudt, C. 2005. Wood and society. In R. M. Rowell (ed.), *Handbook of Wood Chemistry and Wood Composites*. Boca Raton, Florida: CRC Press.

Searchinger, T., S. Hamburg, J. Melillo, W. Chameides, P. Havlik, D. Kammen, G. Likens, R. Lubowski, M. Obersteiner, M. Oppenheimer, G. Robertson, W. Schlesinger, and G. Tilman. 2009. Fixing a critical climate accounting error. *Science* 326: 527–28.

Sedjo, R. A. 2010. The Biomass Crop Assistance Program (BCAP): Some implications for the forest industry. Discussion Paper 10-22, March. Washington, D.C.: Resources for the Future.

Smith, W. B., P. D. Miles, C. H. Perry, and S. A. Pugh. 2009. Forest resources of the United States, 2007. General Technical Report WO-78. Washington, D.C.: USDA Forest Service.

Spelter, H., and D. Toth. 2009. North America's wood pellet sector. Research Paper FPL-RP-656. USDA Forest Service, Forest Products Laboratory.

Sydor, T., and B. C. Mendell. 2008. Transaction evidence analysis: Stumpage prices and risk in central Georgia. *Canadian Journal of Forest Research* 38: 239–46.

Sydor, T., B. Mendell, and A. Hamsley. 2009. A method to track the forest industry in Georgia. *Georgia Forestry Today* May/June 5(3): 30–31.

Technology Review. 2010. Briefing: Fuels. September/October.

The Economist. 2008. The power and the glory: A special report on energy. June 21.

U.S. Department of Energy. 2011. *U.S. billion-ton update: biomass supply for a bioenergy and bioproducts industry*. R.D. Perlack and B.J. Stokes (Leads), ORNL/TM-2011/224. Oak Ridge, Tennessee: Oak Ridge National Laboratory.

U.S. Department of Agriculture. 2010. Proposed rule: Biomass Crop Assistance Program. Federal Register 75(25): 6264–6288, February 8.

Walker, T. (ed.). 2010. Massachusetts biomass sustainability and carbon policy study: Report to the Commonwealth of Massachusetts Department of Energy Resources. Manomet Center for Conservation Sciences. Natural Capital Initiative Report NCI-2010-03. Brunswick, Maine.

Westbrook, J. M., W. Greene, & R. Izlar, 2007. Utilizing forest biomass by adding a small chipper to a tree-length southern pine harvesting operation. *Southern Journal of Applied Forestry* 31(4): 165–169.

Williams, M. 1992. *Americans and their forests: A historical geography*. Cambridge: Cambridge University Press.

Zerbe, J. 2006. Thermal energy, electricity, and transportation fuels from wood. *Forest Products Journal* 56(1): 6–14.

Zerbe, J., and K. Skog. 2007. Sources and uses of wood for energy. Madison, Wisconsin: USDA Forest Service, Forest Products Laboratory.

Brooks Mendell and Amanda Hamsley Lang have coauthored studies of the volume and availability of wood raw materials for energy, the status and progress of wood bioenergy projects, and the potential consequences of legislation for the evolution of wood bioenergy markets. As part of their ongoing research at Forisk Consulting, they track announced and operating wood-using bioenergy projects in the United States.

Amanda Hamsley Lang is senior consultant at Forisk and managing editor of *Wood Bioenergy US*. In addition to leading Forisk's wood bioenergy research program and supporting strategy consulting projects, she teaches workshops and delivers presentations related to tracking and evaluating wood bioenergy markets. Her background includes operations experience with International Paper and award-winning forestry operations research at the University of Georgia under Dale Greene. As part of her research, Amanda speaks with dozens of wood-using project managers, researchers, and contacts on a monthly basis. She received BS and MS degrees in forest resources from the University of Georgia.

Brooks Mendell is president of Forisk and vice president of research. His 20 years of experience include roles in forestry operations with Weyerhaeuser, in forest industry consulting with Accenture, and in academia as a member of the forestry and finance faculties at the University of Georgia. An award-winning speaker, he has also published more than 70 books and articles on topics related to wood bioenergy, global forestry markets, timberland investments, timber REITs, forestry operations, and business communications. He earned BS and MS degrees at the Massachusetts

Institute of Technology, an MBA at the University of California, and a PhD in forest finance at the University of Georgia.

ABOUT FORISK CONSULTING

Forisk is a management consulting and research firm specializing in the forestry and timberland sectors. Forisk advises senior executives in areas such as business strategy, asset and market due diligence, timber market analysis and risk, and organizational development. It conducts organic research on the strategy of timberland investment, including macro factors and price forecasting, emerging markets for wood, and timberland ownership. Forisk's bioenergy research program includes the screening and ranking of wood bioenergy projects, as well as detailed studies evaluating the market and investment implications of alternative technologies. Forisk publishes *Wood Bioenergy US*, which tracks, screens, and analyzes the wood bioenergy sector in the United States. In 2011, Forisk published *Transportation Fuels from Wood: Investment and Market Implications of Current Projects and Technologies*, which detailed 36 biofuels projects and 12 technology pathways for converting wood raw materials to liquid biofuels.